Wild Counselor

Wild Counselor

1977—The Summer of the Hunt

By Jim Finucan

Lighthouse Point Press
Pittsburgh, Pennsylvania

Wild Counselor:
1977—The Summer of the Hunt
Jim Finucan

Published by Lighthouse Point Press
Pittsburgh, Pennsylvania

www.lighthousepointpress.com

www.wildcounselor.com

ISBN: **978-0-9792998-3-4**

Printed in the United States of America

Dedicated to the loving memory of my father, Patrick James Finucan, who never wavered in giving everything he had to his family.

Oh how
I should like to dream again, to look
over the mist on the horizon and see
the sun—to find my dreams again.
But it's gone forever, or until I
see the face of God.

Pat Finucan

CHAPTER 1

Dim, dusty memory blazed through time, hitting me like a thunderbolt as I gazed at the cover of the notebook Mother handed me. I had not seen it since I was eleven, the summer my dad was homeless. They say fact is stranger than fiction, and that summer proves it. I could never make that stuff up. During the few months of that single summer a psychopath shot at Dad, and when the police took no action, I investigated. My brother, Tim, almost lost his hand in a fight, and my brother, Shawn, took on a larger opponent in a boxing match to end the abuses of a bully. My sister, Deirdre, made a sharp U-turn with her life, and I fell for a girl for the first time. That summer, in the midst of all the madness, I tasted love in the kiss of a Cajun girl who had found her way up to the north woods to visit her drunken daddy.

The moment I saw that notebook, my dad's life flashed before me. I saw him morph from his job as a lawyer when I was a kid, to a homeless, divorced, heartbroken man, crushed by depression, who wandered around sleeping in parks. The vision shifted to seeing him cry at Shawn's gravesite on a twenty-below-zero, January winter day in northern Wisconsin. I saw myself pull him away from that gravesite and back into the car. He shook with grief and looked out the back window like we had buried his oldest son alive. Finally, I recalled how he bravely cracked jokes with his last gasp as he lay dying from emphysema. And I remembered leaving the hospital room, not knowing it was the last time I would ever speak to him.

The notebook Mom handed me was a powder blue Mead one-subject, with a crease through the middle where it had been folded to fit in my back pocket. Across the front I had written *The Ballad of Gross Joe* in sloppy handwriting that would do credit to a doctor. That handwriting was young and joyous, reflecting my perpetual state of living at full speed.

I had things to do at that age. The adventure of life was in full swing. *Today I felt tired just thinking about it all.*

The notebook felt like a message from the past that I had written to myself, delivered through a time portal—like a science fiction story.

When I flipped through it, I felt the touch of my own hand from so many years ago, and I felt affectionate understanding toward the boy. I had been just a kid, but had taken on so much, without getting discouraged. I had tried to help my dad with his mental illness, though I didn't know anything about it. I had been a boy having fun in the summer, yet fighting desperately for my life, and handled it without self-pity because I didn't know anything else.

"I am always finding these lying around," Mom said to me. "You have notebooks in the bookshelves and in boxes in the basement, and I found this one in a file cabinet. You were always writing. What are you working on these days?"

"I am working on a novel," I replied, my mind touching the still-tender memory of my father's recent passing.

When I examined the notebook from 1977, I found bits of thoughts and sketches in the margins, like a guy leaning out the window of a building giving the finger with a bubble of speech saying, "Hey, Mr. Bonick!" It was the release of some insult that I had thought twice to make in real life, so it settled on my notebook. "Write a dead Indian ghost story" was scrawled across the top of a page, in red ink from a Bic pen, with a rough outline begun beneath it.

The outline was the story of a boy fighting a weird world of the undead by himself, looking for his friends whom he hoped were not dead, or worse—zombies.

There was a marmalade stain on a page, and the wire that bound the paper had been unwound where I had tried to jam the

Bic pen into the wire spiral, so I could carry the notebook and pen all in one.

I had kept a log of some of my thoughts and experiences, experimented with a detective character I wanted to develop, and even wrote some poetry.

The diary entries were startling to me, and as I flipped through them, I gained a tender sympathy for the young boy I had been. The youth had been naive but unflinching and as I sat down with it, I wondered if I had lost something through the years. I felt the erosion that can occur with time on the inner wall of the soul, when age brushed against it, like a tree branch on a rooftop.

As I handled the soft, worn paper, I felt the corridor of time behind me, heard doors closing on options, and felt the outcome of choices. I also felt the slouch in my spine and the brittleness of my bones in comparison to the young hand that scrawled so many thoughts and dreams so many years ago.

I felt the disappointment of unharnessed potential within me.

For the hand that wrote these messages, the world was full of possibilities and wonder. I felt the touch of the boy I left behind, back there, who lived in this very house, in such a different world, and yet still in the same place as I sat now.

The boy reached out to me through the pages—his fingertips touched mine on the paper, through the pen. A pen, the device that was still so important to me that I always carried one, and in that moment I rode the time machine back to him. I felt him reach out to remind me that the magic of summer presented itself every year to those who understood that adventure was the diet of the hero. He called to me through a time machine—this notebook—to remember the wonderment of life and to struggle to remain a child until the last breath.

In that summer, I struggled to contain my powerful imagination that still takes me places and has propelled me through the darkest times in strange ways.

Dad was homeless the summer of 1977, and many years after that. When I needed to find him, I would fly around town on my bike, looking in the parks where he might be sleeping under his Indian horse blanket, balled up in a fetal position in a coma-like sleep that was his only reprieve from his depression-plagued mind.

On the last day of school, before summer vacation began, I found him in the center of Normal Park, a big, wide-open, block-long field in the center of town, off Center Avenue. I headed over to the sleeping man in the park. I had to wake him up.

Sleep is such a wonderful thing.

"Dad?" I called. I repeated it a few more times before his eyes fluttered and he came out of it.

"Yes?" he answered, looking around like he didn't remember where he was.

"Mom told me to tell you that Gertie had a stroke last night and she is in the hospital." He blinked again and pushed the top half of his body up off the hard ground.

"Oh, no," he said and rubbed his hand through his premature gray mop of thick hair, the same I have now.

My father had been a lawyer before he became homeless. He had been a good one that people sought after. His tactics of fearlessly taking the opposition of a client was rare in the industry. His ability to legally analyze a problem, then lay out a legal strategy that realistically estimated the weaknesses and next moves of opponents, made him a legend as a street lawyer that could be found in the small town.

But Dad was an alcoholic and it caused the downfall of his marriage. When he became injured in the divorce, he lost his ability to work; therefore, the law practice.

When I was eleven, the summer of 1977, Dad had hit rock bottom. He was suffering from severe depression and could only wander around in a form of mental anguish, at times, hanging on moment by moment.

He would walk the sidewalks with a downcast look. The load of the world seemed to drape over him and he dragged his sorrow like a chain.

That summer, the loathsome classroom of confinement was over and long sunny days soon offered liberation from the slavery of forced education that I had detested.

My grandfather, Jim Finucan, graduated from Columbia University and settled here to open his optometrist office in 1922. He died before I ever knew him. Old people in this town, when they heard my name, often cocked their heads like they were remembering something and would say, "Your dad gave me my first eyeglasses."

"That would be my grandpa," I would correct.

My dad, born in this town, was a lawyer for ten years before he slid into a world of mental illness.

My mother had remarried a kind, patient, hard-working man who was a plumber. He could fix anything, and that was good because we kids were a reckless bunch. He loved my mom and that made him an immediate mainstay. He often worked in the basement on projects using power tools while Public Radio played in the background. He let me putz around with his tools and I also developed a love for the jazz music that played over the radio.

Dad haunted the town like a ghoul. He slept in the parks, wandered around the streets and hung out in the community areas of town, and when his mind was not too tortured, he read. But mostly, he lived in a state of pain that prevented him from conversing with others.

The early morning held a chill and the dew was slick on the grass. As the cars passed by, one honked at me. Faces in the car windows looked at us, displaying everything from casual disinterest to disgust and amazement.

I didn't care. I never did care too much what people thought. Most of us only think about ourselves anyway.

"Well, that now, on top of everything else," Dad said, his despair making it sound like two sentences. I stood there over my bike watching the cars go by. He pulled his legs up and stared down at the ground. "Oh no, mama." A car honked and a voice called out something.

"Ok, you had better get going," Dad said. You are going to school, aren't you?"

"Yeah, it's the last day before summer vacation. What will you do today?"

"I don't know."

He moved to his knees and started rolling up the little blanket that he slept on. I stepped on the pedal and the bike rolled me away toward the school. I hesitated, feeling like I was leaving him behind in despair, alone. But I was going to be late.

The dog would be out by now. I glanced at the small can of *Halt!* dog repellent that I taped to the handle bars of my bike two weeks ago. Dad had given it to me when I told him about the dog.

The temperature was about 54 degrees. I cranked down on the bike pedals to gain momentum so that I could blast past the brown house that had the big dog. As I came over a small hill, I saw it sitting in perfect, alert pose, watching me approach. It was waiting for me to get closer before running after me. It had been bred to be a perfect predator.

I aimed the bike down the road and stood up to give weight to the pedals. The bike moved from side-to-side beneath me.

When the dog moved, it blasted at me like a cannon ball, angling at me, to intercept. The German Shepherd-and-Lab mix made for a genetic killing machine, and it fired itself off at me.

The dog's back legs rolled forward, handing off momentum to the front legs and then extending perfectly into a graceful attack, moving at fifty miles an hour, minimum. It was a living arrow of fang with wolf ancestry.

There was no adult to stop whatever would happen here. There were no safety rules or laws to protect me from this animal that saw me as prey. The only two relevant forces in the world at this moment were me and the dog. I was acutely aware of this fact in that moment.

The dog bared its fangs, pulling back the skin over the teeth and snarled. It matched my speed for a moment, and then gained on me easily with a desire for blood.

My hand came off the handle bars and tore loose the black electrician's tape I used to keep the small can of *Halt!* on the chrome handle bar. My thumb found the safety on the top. My legs worked the pedals two more times. The dog closed in. I sprayed just before its teeth seized down on my calf. The liquid sprayed out in a thin stream of concentrated white deterrent that hosed into the dog's eyes, mouth, and nose.

The effect was instant and joyous. The animal yelped in surprise and veered off from me with a muzzleful of the pepper concentration. A few people glanced in my direction, not sure of what had just happened. When I glanced over my shoulder, I saw it rolling on the grass by the roadside, arching its back to grind its muzzle in the turf.

I flew down the street with a sense of empowerment. I had not been victimized. I had made a decision and took action. The can of *Halt!* rested in my light windbreaker jacket pocket and gave me a feeling of protection.

School was St. Roberts—the Catholic school. I parked the bike in the rack. The bell had not rung yet; I could still make it. As I crossed the yard, I noticed three older classmen moving toward the door from another direction. Ken Franklin was among them and he noticed me.

"Hey, where do you think you're going?" he said to me. He was a prick, but had never given me any trouble before. Now it seemed like today was my day to have his team on me. They moved toward me. One veered off to move around behind me. The other two split left, big smiles on their faces with prey in sight. Franklin moved to intercept me like the dog had just a few minutes earlier.

What they had in mind, I couldn't really tell you, a mild beating with a punch, then a few kicks when you hit the ground, was the standard operating procedure for Franklin and his team; I had seen them beat up Ben Taylor. And I heard they did it to Rick Pendleton.

I felt the first two punches, glancing with no real impact on my head and cheek, and tried to counter-strike, but Franklin was taller than me, and I received two more blows without being able to score any contact.

The other two moved in around me and I felt a kick to the back of my leg. There was no way to escape. The solution to my desperation was clearly the weight in my pocket where I had put the can of mace. In one, smooth, fluid motion, I pulled it out and flipped off the little safety, and for the second time in eight minutes, depressed the red button on top.

The thin stream hit Franklin's face. I kept the button down and as the stream flowed, I moved it around at the heads of the other boys attacking me. They collapsed under the liquid fire. The wind blew the chemical around the school parking lot and several other people had to be taken to the hospital for a flushing by the time it was all over with.

They made a big deal out of it. When I reached the door and intended to go in, Mrs. Kramer, who must have witnessed it, ran up to me. She was one of the last teachers in the world to mess with. When yelling at Keith Cann, she had poked him on the nose with her index finger so hard that his eyes had watered all day. She grabbed my jacket collar and yelled in my face, "What was that? What was that you sprayed on them?" She was overdramatizing it, like it might have been a chemical weapon in development by the government. I produced the can from my pocket in response, and she snatched it from my palm and spun away to read it.

Being the last day of school, they sent me home with a stern suggestion that perhaps the following year the public school would be a better fit for me.

Mom thought about sending me to the Merrill Junior High next fall.

When Dad came to get me out of school earlier in the year, he would appear in the window of the classroom to the side of the teacher. He sometimes made a face in the window. The kids roared with laughter at his unkempt hair tousled around his head, and he would give a silly, zany expression, rolling his eyes up and sticking out his tongue.

The teacher would notice and open the door of the classroom.

"Is Jamie here?" Dad asked at the door. "I have to take him out of school. We have an appointment."

"Are you his father?" the teacher replied, looking at his worn, too-short, canvas shorts and sweatshirt with the arms cut off at the shoulders.

"That's my dad, Sister Marie. I have to go now." The other kids would look at me in envy, thinking "if only they could trade the long day in a classroom for a day anywhere but here," they would. I made for the door and felt like I was making a jail break.

"Let's go to the park. I have some steaks we can grill out at Riverside," Dad would say as we shuffled quickly down the hallway.

But today, after macing several students, I was kicked out of school and, with my few notebooks under my arm, I left the classroom for the last time. I glanced at the faces. Expressions ranged from concern to excitement at having something unusual happen. I walked out to the bike rack with my book bag and watched the ambulance take the last of the students away to get their eyes flushed. I remember thinking how odd it was to have the day ahead of me that I had not planned. I rode away from the school for the last time. Summer had begun and was starting off to be a real wing-dinger.

* * *

The blue notebook that Mom had found gave me insight on my early writing. I wrote:

The Ballad of Gross Joe

Gross Joe was rolling down the highway in his Bonneville when the windshield was struck and a spider-web pattern formed in the safety glass. Joe flinched and the Bonneville weaved into the other lane, almost causing a head-on crash with a Mack truck traveling in the opposite direction.

Joe corrected the car just in time. The rear-view mirror showed a black sedan following him with two people in the front seat—one leaning out the window, tucked behind an extended rifle.

Joe swerved the Bonneville and another bullet cracked through the windows of the car, brushing air against his ear.

He punched his foot down on the accelerator and it lurched as it shifted down to grab a gear, and then up as it sped. Joe coughed a few times. Fifteen years of smoking was not going to waste. He hacked up a big greenie and let it roll up from his lungs, and then gather in his throat. The thick wad of phlegm had a meaty core of cigarette tar that felt like a walnut growing in his throat. When it was ready, he gargled it up and rolled it in his mouth to form it into a circular blob.

Another bullet punched through the window, destroying his rear-view mirror. Joe rolled down the window, then gobbed it out, launching it up in a high trajectory, so it would be guided by wind and drop in line with the path of the car behind him.

The phlegm wad hit the windshield of the black sedan dead center in the view of the driver—squashing like a rotten peach across the glass. The pursuing car veered back and forth in the road. The massive, sticky glob spread out in the wind to block the driver's vision. The passenger with the rifle knocked against the dashboard, then the car door.

"What the hell is the matter with you?" the gunman yelled at the driver in a thick Russian accent.

"I tell you, I cannot see," the driver yelled back.

Inside Joe's car, he was cool, looking at the driver's side mirror. "Wait for it...wait for it...come on."

The gunman tried to hang out the window for another shot, but withdrew, and was hanging onto the dashboard for balance as the car veered.

The driver turned on the windshield wiper and smeared the tar and phlegm wad across the remaining vision of the windshield area. The vision factor went to zero in a paste of smeared, lunged, tobacco scuz. The black sedan swerved from one side of the road to the other. It crossed the center line, over-compensated, then hit the ditch at seventy miles an hour.

The sedan's front-end caught in the ditch and the back end lifted. It flipped end-over-end, until it came to rest on its top with gasoline spilling over it. When the car exploded behind him, Joe took his foot off the accelerator. He looked to where his rear view mirror had been, but had to switch his glance to his side mirror to see parts of the car flying in all directions from the fireball that erupted.

"Fuck you for breaking my windshield," Joe yelled out loud and slammed down the accelerator.

* * *

My friend, Mike, lived a few blocks away. He was in my Catholic school and was a child of a divorced family like mine. He had a light frame with red, wispy hair and the mythical presence of the ginger in the class, like Piggy in the *Lord of the Flies*. Mike's demeanor was light-hearted. He was quick to crack up at a humor attempt, and more than once, in school, that got us in trouble. But he was also cocky and lipped off to kids that were bigger than him. I understood that this was part of his spirit of adventure or revolt, of which I never figured out.

There was an outrage within him at the world and he would not be silent in complying with it. I had learned to keep my mouth shut from having older brothers; don't cock off to people unless you want to have a fight. He was an only child so there were lessons that only the brutal side of the world could teach him about pride.

Our walk took us past the Holiday gas station where an older boy came out of the store and looked at Mike.

"Hey, light bulb eater," he said and cuffed at Mike's head. Years ago, Mike had touched a hot light bulb to his lips and walked around for a week with a kisser that looked like he was wearing clown make-up. He looked like he was sucking on a pair of those big candy lips.

"Knock it off," Mike said and ducked late.

We made our way across Normal Park, where I had woken up my dad earlier that day.

"Did you hear Erik Krumel is out of the Lincoln Boy School?" Mike said gravely.

"No." My stomach dropped a quarter of an inch. "Where did you hear that?"

"Buck Riggs saw him and Ron Thompson coming out of the A&W. He said when they got out of the door, Krumel punched a kid right in the face for looking at him in the parking lot."

"Great." My mood suddenly plunged.

"He told Riggs he is looking for you. He said your older brother, Tim, punched out his older brother and the whole family wants Erik to kick your ass, bad."

"Not what I want to hear," I heard myself say. Erik Krumel was bigger, taller than I was, and outweighed me by about forty pounds. My hand went to the pocket where the mace can had been but its cylindrical comfort was gone, confiscated by Mrs. Kramer after the incident on the playground.

My summer began with an impending sense of doom.

I didn't have to wait long for something to take my mind off it. We were apparently easy to find on that cloudy day, because two older boys aimed to intersect with us fast at 45 degrees. They were clearly moving in our direction, looking at us.

"We got trouble coming up." I remembered the flight of the dog in my direction. It was a day for it.

"Oh shit, its Hartson and his buddy," Mike said.

"Are we having a go of it here?" I asked fast. Both opponents were bigger than us, older as well.

"No, let me handle this. It has nothing to do with you," Mike said. They moved right to us.

"Hi, Chris," Mike spoke up. "I told ya' I wouldn't cock off to you anymore and I haven't." He got this out before Chris punched him in the stomach and shoved him down.

When Mike hit the ground, Hartson jumped on him and put his knee on his head.

"Quit cocking off. Do you understand that? Do you? Quit cocking off!" Hartson yelled and punched Mike in the side, hard. His buddy stared at me; I gave it back to him.

"I won't—I said I wouldn't and I won't," Mike yelled from under the knee of Hartson, who punched him in the stomach and knocked the air out of Mike. I moved forward; the buddy stepped in my way.

"You got something to do?" the buddy asked me. Mike wasn't fighting, so I would have both of these clowns to deal with.

"I'm doing it," I replied. Sometimes a confrontation could be avoided by direct eye contact. Hartson's buddy inched up in my face and searched my eyes for fear. He found none. The day he did, I would jump in front of a train. I had older brothers in my house and we scrapped near-to-death over the prize in the bottom of a Lucky Charms box. This kid was a punk.

Hartson punched Mike in the side one more time, the blow making a hollow sound. Then he got up off Mike and started walking away like he was moving on to something better in life.

Mike got up from the ground and picked up his Brewers baseball cap. He beat it against his leg a few times to clean it and glanced at me in embarrassment. I felt like I let him down. He took a few breaths, hunched with his hands on his knees, and watched them move away.

I could see what he was thinking and I knew what he was going to do.

He gathered himself and his pride.

"Get ready to run," he called when he had his wind. "Hartson, you suck, you punch like a girl and your mother dresses you funny," he yelled out, and the two boys stopped in mid-stride. "Your dad called. He wants his sperm back. In fact, the whole world wants him to get it back." Mike flipped him the bird while looking him right in the eye. "I know I sure do."

I got it. This was the way he protected his dignity.

They broke into a run at us.

"Run," Mike said, and bolted off running across the wide-open park. If I didn't run, I would face them both alone, upper classmen of bigger stature. I watched them advance, and glanced at Mike, his image getting smaller as he almost reached the edge of the park.

I decided that my dignity was something to set aside. I followed. We ran like kids did. We ran everywhere we wanted to go. We left them in the dust. I passed Mike on the sidewalk, then blasted ahead thirty feet. Mike poured it on, caught up with me, then inched past. He was fast. To be fast was a high honor in our culture. I dug down deep within myself, sprinted hard, and caught and passed him, my lungs aflame in my chest from lack of oxygen.

I gained about ten feet of ground and held it until we got to Rexall, a pharmacy with one of the last soda fountains in it. At the counter, you could get a cherry Coke, a hot dog, a milk shake, or a burger. Old men sat at the counter drinking coffee, discussing the weather any time of day. Before we could go in, we had to catch our breath. Leaning on the building, I gasped for air.

The door opened and Jenny Wilson walked out of the drug store with her mother, who was pretty and wearing a tight dress and high heels. I could see where Jenny got her looks. Jenny looked at me for a moment. I smiled and she looked away. Jenny's mom noticed and asked her who I was as they walked away.

"It's the boy whose daddy lives in the park," I heard her say. I felt the smile slide off my face.

We walked into the drug store, passing a rack of corn cob pipes, a shelf with some Hi Karate cologne and baseball cards, and then a rack of comics. I stopped to pick up the latest copy of Spiderman to see if Morbius was in this issue and thumbed through it in front of the wire rack. A radio played Johnny Rivers "Swaying to the Music" from the grill behind the counter.

The place was alive with local conversation. Five men were at the soda fountain drinking coffee and talking, two ladies were in the next isle discussing an upcoming birthday party, people were paying for things at the noisy till, and the bells of the cash drawer rang with small town business.

I moved away from the comic book rack and to the mystical monolith that stood against the wall. The six-foot-tall scale made of ancient cast iron had a glass case on top that held the manikin of a gypsy imprisoned within it. For a nickel, it not only told your weight but also displayed your fortune in a water filled glass bubble. To a kid, it seemed to have been forged in the fires of a tribe of warlock blacksmiths in Eastern Europe.

It stood like a menacing figure in the room and beckoned any passersby to tempt fate and learn their fortune. "Could any of us handle knowing such a thing?" I wondered as I stared at it. Perhaps there was a good reason why the future is blind to us. Then I did what I did every time I came into Rexall; I stood on the scale.

The small platform moved slightly, but the needle didn't budge and the fortune didn't display. I had not put a nickel in it. It looked like it wanted to play with me but the gentle rocking of the platform beneath my shoes was the only thing that moved on the scale. I rocked on it gently, back and forth, feeling it defy gravity in its way. I stepped off to the hard-tiled floor of the drug store, back on earth.

The eyes of the gypsy seemed to follow me from a bloody altar. Zoltar watched to see if I would reach for a nickel, drop it in the tin slot, and light up the bulb at the top. I had stepped on it. Now it knew my fortune and had weighed me in its mystical medium way.

"Are you afraid, kid?" I imagined if it could communicate with me telepathically, Zoltar would ask, "Aren't you the boy that was running across the park today—running away from a fight after your friend cocked off?"

Mike approached and looked on the scale in wonderment. Then he did what we all did, but he did it with more gusto, and he jumped on the scale. Mike watched the needle move up in a half promise for a second, but settle back like a closing middle finger. In the glass bubble, the big dice chunk with words of prophecy didn't face up. Zoltar, the mystic, had seen a few snot-nosed kids that didn't want to put a nickel in the slot.

A few people glanced our way.

Mike jumped onto the device like a cowhand breaking a spirited colt. He pumped his legs and rocked the scale. When he almost lost his balance, he grabbed it with both hands and continued the assault. The metal ground and gears rattled in ringing revolt. Zoltar was getting his ass kicked by the kid who cocked off to people in the park.

Whatever pain was in his life was being directed at the scale of fortune. We had the attention of everyone in the store. But Zoltar had a few tricks up his sleeve.

Mike's furious crescendo came to an abrupt ending when a fat woman stormed through the staring customers with fire in her eyes. She plowed through the browsing patrons like they were cardboard cut outs, then fixed a furious gaze on Mike as he jumped one more time on the scale.

I had no chance to warn him.

"What do you think you are doing?" she yelled at the side of Mike's head like a drill sergeant. "I live downstairs and I thought you were going to come right through the ceiling on me!" Mike stepped off the scale and looked at her in horror.

The pharmacy was still, like a millpond.

"Did you ever think what might be underneath the floor before you start jumping up and down on something? I was sleeping down there; you are right above an apartment. Use your head for something besides keeping your ears from snapping together." Her goiter blubbered below her chin, shaking its own fist at Mike in anger. She shamed him by giving him a pause so that he could respond if he so had the nuts.

Mike did not. She was too close to cock off.

"You just walk up to the machine and start jumping on it because you are too cheap to put a nickel in the slot? Was it worth a nickel to wake me up? I have a shift to work in three hours!" The woman reached into her baggy, stained pants pocket and produced some change and threw it at him. Coins flew in a fan of metal and made tinkling sounds as they flipped and scattered across the tiled floor.

Mike flinched.

"Here's a nickel. Was it worth it? Not to me it wasn't!" She stared at Mike and then swung her gaze at me.

"What are your names?" she hollered.

"Mike Stevens and Jamie Finucan," Mike replied. She turned on me like a turret.

"Is your dad the lawyer who went nuts?"

"Nuts—like you right now?" I asked.

"Both of you get out of here. I don't want to see you around here ever again." She turned to bowl her way through the stunned customers.

"We wouldn't piss on this place if it was on fire," I said extra loud from the fire in my soul.

When Mike got to the door and before the lady was out of range, he turned and yelled: "Hey, fatso, maybe it's you who is shaking the floor now! You suck, and your mother dresses you funny, and your dad wants his sperm back." Then he stuck out his tongue, made a fart sound, and pushed his way out the door, fast.

But the doorway wasn't clear. Mike barreled into an old man wearing a fedora. They collided hard with unexpected contact and tumbled on the sidewalk, knocking over the sandwich board sign announcing the roast beef sandwich and French onion soup special of the day. The old man landed hard on the sidewalk with his arms extended, surrendering hopelessly to gravity. His fedora skidded on its crown on the cement to stop at the base of a parking meter.

I thought of the change hitting the floor in the drug store a few moments ago.

Mike got up and ran away. I tried to help the old man get up, but he shook off my hand.

"Damn kids, don't you look where you're going?" he said in a painful stammer.

I walked away from the scale of misfortune and the fat lady with no class. I didn't want to run anymore. A rage smoldered within me. An older man stepped up beside me and touched my shoulder. It was Judge Schnabel; he had hurried to catch up with me.

"I know your father. He is a brilliant man. I have seen him in action. In his day, he was something to admire. I have a tremendous amount of respect for him. If there is anything I can do for you, young man, come and see me," he said.

"I will. Thank you, sir." I turned and kept walking in a state of wonder. I looked up the street and saw a head with red hair on it stick out from behind the brick wall of the fabric store. Mike was hiding and waiting about a half block up the street.

Something cracked up inside me at the thought of this character having such a hard time. I saw his struggle similar to mine. We were space cowboys. I cracked up laughing as I walked toward him.

"Why didn't you run?" he asked.

"If you cock off like that to someone, stand there and take them on. I don't run away like that anymore. I don't and, when you're with me, you don't. Got it?" I felt this coming out of me and it tasted true.

"Why not?"

"Say anything you have to, to survive. Get it off your chest. I get it, go ahead, but then we stand there, and take the consequences. I won't run off on you. I'll stand there with you, but don't you shoot your mouth off anymore unless you are going to back it up."

"All right. Fair enough," he said, looking at the ground as we turned to walk side-by-side.

"Come on, let's go catch bullheads down in the park," I suggested.

"No, I'm going home. My mom's making me beans and wieners for lunch." I had been at his house and had that meal—Van Camps beans with hot dogs cut up in it, Mike's favorite lunch. In the roaring silence of being alone I thought of the day's events and felt the bruise of social interaction.

I spent the rest of the afternoon with a small fishing rod dangling a worm in front of a brook trout in Stanges Park, retreating to simple action.

CHAPTER 2

I never travel without my diary. One should always have something sensational to read in the train.

Oscar Wilde

It is the mind
That is the mind
Confusing the mind.
Do not leave the mind,
O mind,
To the mind.

The Book of Five Rings, Miyamoto Musashi

The bliss of summertime in north central Wisconsin is magnified by its brief span. The cold winters, chilly wet falls, and drizzly springs give elation to a period of three months of perfect temperatures and long, sunny days.

My parents divorced when I was in third grade. Mom remarried and we moved from Lake Pesobic to the City of Merrill. We lived in a big white house surrounded by majestic pine trees across the street from the Dairy Queen.

The Dairy Queen, which employed the cutest girls, was located right on Center Avenue, a central hub of the City of Merrill, where people driving past could see who was out and about.

I walked across the street to the Dairy Queen.

My step-dad, Bob, liked dogs, especially Springer Spaniels and there was always one in the house. Springer Spaniels are more emotionally sensitive than other dogs. They graced the house with a special kindness and each one of them was a good friend and had a relationship with each person in the house.

If God has a dog, it is a Springer Spaniel.

That summer our Springer was Gus. He had an eye that didn't focus right, and when he looked at you he cocked his head to the side to get you in focus and he gave the impression that he was challenging what you might have been saying to him.

With the beginning of summer, I wanted to kick it off with a cherry, old-fashioned soda, so I walked across the street and found Gus already there. He was sitting beside a yellow pickup truck watching a big man with blond hair eating a cherry-covered ice cream cone. Gus was focused on the man as he bit through the cherry-dipped covering on the cone, then licked at the soft serve.

The driver of the truck was watching Gus, showing it to him, teasing the dog. Gus watched him with focused attention in his cockeyed expression. His focus was so sharp. If he could have studied engineering with that level of concentration, he could have solved the mystery of the pyramids.

I stuck my head in the window of the ice cream stand to get a look at who was working and smell the sweet aroma of caramel and sugar that rolled out the little window. That aromatic scent accentuated the lovely vision of Jenny Wilson. She was rolling the soft serve into a cone and making perfect bulges in the cone to give it a Michelin Man shape.

Her attention was focused on her activity so she was unaware of the level of perfection of grace in each movement she was achieving. Jenny's face held a glow of beauty from her big eyes, feminine jaw line, and lips that held almost a constant pucker. She turned gracefully and handed the ice cream cone to the customer at the other window. She took the money and as she was making change she glanced at my head sticking in the window.

A slight smile touched her full lips. She had glanced at me during the most challenging aspect of the sale—the making of the change. That meant something. That meant she liked me.

Yes, she was two years older than me, but that didn't mean that she was out of my reach. I knew lots of people that were happy with the woman being older. In fact, my mom had just married a guy that was at least seven years younger than her.

"I said, what are you getting?" John Purcell appeared beside me. His bike was lying on the ground with the back tire spinning. I had not seen him come up.

"What would you like?" Jenny asked.

"A cherry, old-fashioned soda," I replied.

"Isn't that what you got yesterday?" she asked with a smile.

"One a day is my limit," I nodded, thinking that was pretty witty.

"Hey, Gus is begging from Derrick Lawton's truck," John said. I looked behind me and saw Gus sitting on the pavement, stretching his nose toward the yellow truck next to him. The man eating the ice cream cone in the yellow pickup looked down in spite. Derrick Lawton was a man who was tall and broad in shoulder with a haggard face. He wore a mean expression on his face that looked like a challenge.

He plowed his face into the ice cream cone with an aggressive striking motion of his neck and head.

"You don't get nothing!" Derrick yelled at Gus as he ate the ice cream cone.

Gus's retribution was swift. Seemingly in slow motion, he reared up and put both of his clawed feet on the surface of the yellow-painted truck door and dug them in; and then he let his weight pull him down to the ground.

It sounded like razor blades on steel, emitting a high squeaky sound that stopped everyone in the motion they were doing.

He looked magnificent, even as I stared in horror. A well-muscled hunting dog, the Springer Spaniel is bred for flushing birds, springing up over ground cover and appearing like a gazelle in brush, thistle, and cattail to flush out the birds that are hiding.

That dog is a testimony to what dog breeders can accomplish when they mess with genetics.

I saw that beauty in the dog, and I also saw the scratches he put in the paint. Derrick Lawton threw the cone at the dog and grabbed the door handle to open it. Gus caught the half ice cream cone in midair and clenched it while running away, low to the ground, his tail extending straight back, in what I recognized as hunter's jubilation.

Lawton piled out of the truck and ran after my dog, but Gus kept his cool and ran, not across the street to his home, but down the street past the Pizza Hut. Gus, The Wonder Dog, knew better than to lead the assailant to his own home.

After Lawton strode with perpetual motion back to the parking lot, he looked around at the nine customers standing in the lot.

"Whose fucking dog was that?" he asked. His gaze swept across me and it felt like a searchlight.

"Sir, you need to watch your language on this property," a woman said from the window. She was the manager.

"I'm gonna kill that fucking dog and you can pay for the paint job on my truck!" he yelled back at the head of the lady sticking through the window.

Lawton looked at the scratch in the yellow paint of his truck and then turned to her to give her the finger. Then he got into his truck and drove off in the direction Gus had run.

"Isn't that your dog?" Jenny asked me in a hushed tone. She leaned in toward me to whisper it.

"That's Gus, the bravest dog in the world," I answered. John and I walked across the street to my family house. I glanced down the road wishing Gus well. The cherry, old-fashioned soda tasted sweet, but I was concerned.

"So what do you know about that guy?" I asked John.

"Derrick Lawton? He went to jail for beating the crap out of a guy with the lid of a trash can. My mom booked him into the jail a few years back. He's is a psychopath."

"He's got it out for my dog. I don't like that."

A shadow passed on us from a cloud in the sky; the breeze picked up and a chill went over my skin.

"You have a bigger problem," John said and looked me in the eyes.

"Yeah?"

"Erik Krumel is out of the Lincoln Hills School for Boys."

"I heard."

"He's all over town punching out people like it was free, and he's looking for you. He punched out Josh Waller in front of the Holiday gas station yesterday. When he was on the ground, Krumel gobbed on him and told him to say 'hi' to you."

"Great."

The tall plastic cup the old-fashioned soda was served in gave up the rest of the rich syrup at the bottom. There was always a cherry at the bottom. I made an effort to enjoy it.

* * *

Sometimes Dad stayed in Riverside Park. He moved around to different parks because the cops would run him out at night. Merrill is known as the City of Parks; it's a tag line because the good tax payers of the community pay for the upkeep of nine beautiful city parks that have been landscaped well to accentuate the natural attraction of the land and northern Wisconsin attributes.

Riverside Park stretches out on the southern edge of town along the Wisconsin River. At the foot of the bridge and the beginning of the park stands the haunted mansion of T.B. Scott.

The mansion's chilling history is well known to the community. Before T. B. Scott built one of the dozen or so mansions of the lumber baron era, the town was occupied by Chippewa Indians. The particular hill just outside of town was the place where a Chippewa Indian chief, who was also a powerful medicine man, cursed all the white men after his daughter was made sick by one of the settlers of the era.

The story could be heard two ways: she was raped and killed by a logger, or she got influenza. Whatever happened, the old Indian did something with his dark art that stained the ground with hatred, and he cursed the hill.

The dark story of the T. B. Scott Mansion was part of that summer, with so much time spent in the adjacent park. Delores Chilsen Mielke laid the foundation in her short book about the mansion where I got to know the characters like neighbors.[1]

T. B. Scott began building the mansion in 1830; he was a rich lumber baron. Before he moved to Merrill he had been a state senator, a bank president, and was owner of the flourishing T.B. Scott Lumber Company. He died in the mansion at age 57. (Local lore states he was found hanging by a rope from one of the unfinished support beams in the mansion while under construction. I heard that his hands were clenched up in fists so tight they could not be opened. More official accounts say he died suddenly from Bright's disease.)

Scott's wife, Ann, died in the mansion a year later. His son, Walter, inherited the unfinished mansion and took over the plans to see it through to its conclusion. With the death of his father and then his mother, Walter must have been in quite a state of mind, and perhaps that led to his own demise.

Scott went to see the mansion's architect, Mr. Sheldon, about the house plans and to tell the architect that he believed the house was haunted. The two men got into a fight in the Chicago office building. The architect stabbed Scott to death

[1] T.B. Scott Mansion, by Delores Chilsen Mielke—T.B. Scott Free Library, Merrill, Wisc.

with a letter opener in his office. Scott had been telling Sheldon that he was convinced the house was cursed.

After being charged with murder, the architect was acquitted, claiming self-defense. It was taken into account that Mr. Scott was a significantly bigger man than the architect.

In 1893, a Chicago millionaire, Edward Kuechle, bought the house for his summer home. He shortly thereafter lost his money in a California gold mine fraud and was forced to sell the house. He promptly went insane and died shortly thereafter in an insane asylum.

A Chicago business man named John Barsante purchased the building and was on his way to north central Wisconsin to view his new investment by railway when, on route, he was stabbed in the back in Union Station by an assassin from the Black Hand—assassins with organized crime ties. Barsante died before he could see the property.

In 1901, George Gibson, an Illinois land speculator, bought the house, moved up to Merrill and established an office in the mansion. He wasn't in town long when he vanished, walking from his home to the mansion, and his body was never found.

In 1906, Mrs. Felhaber purchased the house and the 39 acres that is now Riverside Park. She was by trade a midwife. While riding by buggy to a client's house, she raced her buggy into a nearby farmhouse driveway and pounded on the door. She felt death approaching, she had stated. She died there before any doctor could arrive.

The estate assigned a caretaker to T.B. Scott Mansion and he looked after the building for many years. He was a man with one arm, from England, named Popcorn Dan. Though he had only one arm, he was known to work hard. He sold popcorn at the local events in Riverside Park from a small cart.

I would think of that guy sometimes when walking through the park.

The concrete slab that was the band stage is still set against the hill that escalates up to the mansion from Riverside Park.

Black steel rails stand out from the hillside to remind anyone still of old performances of the early Merrill City Band, which played to a crowd of people dressed in fancy, old clothes, talking; kids running around wearing knickers or whatever was the clothing of the day; and this whole park being a community center.

It would have been a big deal and the town would have supported a party in Riverside Park, in the shadow of the mansion.

Some of the traveling musicians that came to play at that time were legendary coronet players, the rock stars of their day, performing magnificently with nothing but drilled out shapes of metal for mouthpieces. This was prior to the ability to record sound, so in my imagination I hear them in the still park, throwing it down, at a level with Maynard Ferguson or Miles Davis.

Popcorn Dan missed his home in England. So in 1911, he took a ship back home. He stayed in his home country for a year and in 1912, for a return voyage to America and his job as caretaker of the Scott Mansion, he booked himself a seat on the fated Titanic and was included among the lost on that doomed vessel.

A man staying in the mansion had started walking across the bridge into town on the fourth of July to watch the fireworks in the city. He never made it across the bridge and was never seen again. They dragged the Wisconsin River looking for another occupant of the mansion, but it gave up no corpse.

Finally, the Sisters of the Holy Cross took over the building and had the church perform an actual exorcism that is on record with the diocese of Superior, and erected a cross on the top of the building. The Sisters claim to have driven out the evil spirit.

I rode my bike through the park, recounting the story, stopping at the ancient band stand for a moment to look at it and imagine.

If I don't do enough of that, there will be no sleep. There must be time in every day to imagine. I saw them in period-type dress, enjoying the performance. Kids running around, ladies flirting, distinguished men moving around the crowd and deep in the woods a faint hint of movement. An Indian medicine man stepped behind a tree; he watched in hatred.

I found Dad sitting on the picnic table smoking a Marlboro 100, wearing jeans and a blue hooded sweatshirt that seemed to sprout holes as I watched. He had his legs crossed and was looking at the silent rolling Wisconsin River that passed by the park. I set my bike down and joined him on the table. A Blue Jay gave its call and a robin said something else about the sunshine that was being blocked out by a light cloud cover.

I was one of the few people who could be around Dad a lot. I had learned young, being the youngest of four children, how to make myself small. I had developed a gift for being in the company of the mentally tortured. I had an instinct for knowing when to speak and not to. I said gentle, positive things and used a soothing tone. I let comments go that I didn't want him to expand on or pursue. I had to be careful of mental rabbit trails or the direction of conversation that could lead to an anguishing mental dead end. Nothing was about me. I spoke of simple pleasures and made comments that were pleasant.

That was the way to be around the emotionally injured.

The river seemed to scroll past us like a continuous idea, churning dark water and foam that rubbed on the banks and rocks. Every moment offered a different face, yet without changing; it was moving, yet not making a sound. I sat next to Dad and took in the beauty of the day.

I didn't want to speak—or ruin the moment.

"I was just sitting here thinking about how I screwed up my life," Dad opened up to me. "I lost my wife, my kids, my ability to earn a living, and now people treat me like I'm a disease. No one wants you around when you're poor. I don't know what happened, but it did not go as I planned." He took a drag on the cigarette. Smoke rolled out of his nose.

"It's a good thing I came along then," I replied. "Do you want to go float sticks in the stream off the river and throw rocks at them?"

The early day was warm. A light drizzle was beginning to fall. Dad's sleeping bundle was rolled up next to him by a pack holding his few belongings.

He had a day of urban survival ahead of him

"Your mother doesn't want me around. I went over there to have coffee with her and she treated me like I was bothering her. Sometimes her attitude is sure flaky."

"Well, she did divorce you," I said with my eleven-year-old logic.

"I failed at everything. All the most important decisions that people make in life—those are the ones I really screwed up. The ones you can't undo." He breathed out the smoke in several breaths.

"Then it might be time to move on. Let it be finished business," I suggested. I picked up a twig from a maple tree, broke it, and tied it in a knot with the green bark that stayed connected. I tossed it on the ground and imagined detective Gross Joe picking it up at a crime scene and looking at it closely. Like he found the same broken stick tied in a knot at another crime scene.

"There is no getting over it," Dad said. "It's unfinished business. You just can't go forward because it is still going on inside you."

I had no clue what the hell he was talking about now.

"I remember the moment I fell in love with her. We were having lunch at the Rathskeller in Madison and she turned to say goodbye to me. She was wearing a blue sweater and the sunlight caught her hair, and in that moment she won my heart." The faraway look was in his eyes.

"Did you eat breakfast yet today, Dad?"

The summer day was cloudy; the rain could yet pick up. There was no school and if Dad wasn't going to be fun, I was thinking about finding some friends to swim with. Or Rob Grefe and I could go hunting for rabbits in the pines, then make a rabbit stew in the afternoon.

I thought of the refrigerator at home. Mom had carrots, some celery, and a few potatoes. That was all we needed.

"Naa," he said. Smoke poured out of his nose and mouth like an abstract painting. The birds called out around us again and the river moved by like a gentle old man.

"What are you reading these days?" Dad asked.

"*Treasure Island* by Robert Louis Stevenson and *The Book of Five Rings* by Miyamoto Musashi.

"I like *Treasure Island.* That is a great sea story. How about when they put the black spot on someone, that meant they were going to kill him?"

"Yeah, that is cool." I threw another twisted-up twig toward the river. It didn't make it to the waterline.

"I saw a ghost down here last night," Dad said. My ears perked up.

"Really?"

"Yes, it was a mist with a light in it. It moved down the hill and across the park, first this way, then it moved down to the river. When it got to the river, it vanished. It was spooky. It's beautifully creepy down here at night."

"What was the ghost like?"

"I think it's the Indian chief who cursed the hill. The Indian had the right idea of the white man. They are a bunch of assholes. Anyway, the Indian chief was dancing around a fire. He was painted white with big red streaks of blood down his chest. He was dancing around like this." Dad got up and did an Indian dance jumping from one foot to another and lifting his face up into the drizzling rain. I smiled—a sun-tanned white guy with prematurely gray hair performing a rain dance or something.

"What was the blood from?" I asked.

"He had just bit the head off of a rabbit and was sprinkling it on a fire in front of him. And when he did, the fire hissed and jumped up like it was gasoline."

"Why would it do that?"

"I don't know. But this whole area is cursed. The Scott Mansion is right up there on top of the hill. The chief prowls this park at night; I've seen it. Think of all the bad stuff that has happened to people that lived in that house. These are the grounds that Scott owned."

"I thought only white men couldn't live in the house."

"No, ladies, too. There was a lady who moved in and went for a walk to inspect the grounds, and she was never seen again. They dragged the river for her, too. Never found a trace of her."

"What do you think happened to her?"

"Whatever happened to her, happened right here. These are the grounds."

"Maybe that's who you saw last night, walking around here."

"No, this was the Indian medicine man. I told you, he was standing in the moonlight last night, looking around. If you ever see the mist with a light in it, he appears right after that."

"Did he see you?"

"Well, if he did, he didn't seem to mind. He looked at me, or maybe through me."

"What did he do then?"

"He went back to dancing around the fire—like this." Dad got up again and started dancing around in his best Native-American style. He had no rhythm, but he had some of the movements down enough to give me the idea.

I leaned back and relaxed for a moment, imagining the old medicine man still watching us from a sacred fire pit a few feet away.

"Was it cold down here last night?" I asked.

"It didn't rain, so that was good. My army blanket kept me warm enough. Sleeping on the ground is hard on my back though, and I think sleeping on the ground pulls energy and warmth out of your body. I am going to sleep on the picnic tables. I think that's better for me."

"Where will you stay when it gets cold outside?"

"I'll get out of here—leave this shitty town. The people are assholes here. There are neat places all over. I need to find one. I just wish I had some money." The silence settled on us like the mist. I swatted a mosquito as big as a dime on my leg.

"The social injustice in this country is sickening. The poor eat shit all day long, get mistreated from people, shoved around, not allowed to sleep here, not allowed to loiter there, and always pushed on. And it's not right. All the rich people got the money and they abuse everyone else with it."

"Didn't they earn it though?" I questioned.

"They made their money off the backs of the poor. Look at these window factories in this town. They pay people minimum wage to risk their limbs and take shit from a foreman. I was talking to a guy who got fired for being late. Like the windows wouldn't wait ten minutes."

"There are jobs, and the people who have them are glad to have them. And if they are not happy they can leave and get another job," I responded. A big black ant was crawling across the table. I put my hand out and it walked onto my palm, scouting for something to report back to central command. I could feel its tiny feet on my skin.

"And get another job doing the same thing or something similar. What kind of a chance is that?"

"Well, then they can learn a skill that will give them a different life. Of course they have to work at it, and study, and stuff like that."

"Look at me. I have three college degrees and I am homeless. So much for an education, the yardstick for measuring how civilized a society is, is how it treats its lowest members. We treat the poor like shit in this country. I know I am one of them. One day there will be a revolution, and when it occurs, all these shitheads will get put against the wall and shot," he said in disgust.

"Let's do something." I wanted to break him out of his blue state, hating to hear the socialism crap. It worked; he glanced at me and started thinking about action.

"We could get Richard Putnam's canoe and paddle down the river to Brokaw." He threw it out there. I grabbed it.

"Yeah, that would be great." I was pumped up; we had an action plan now.

"We will need some sandwiches for lunch. This could take the better part of the day," Dad said.

"I'll go home and make two peanut butter and jelly," I said, jumping to my feet.

"I'll go talk to Richard and have him load the canoe on his truck and drop it off for us down here. I'll ask him if he would pick us up in Brokaw when we're done."

"How will he know when we are done?"

"We'll have to find a phone. When we get to Brokaw, we can find a phone."

This was the stuff I liked, taking on a project and moving on it rather than sitting around moping.

"And make mine heavier on the peanut butter and not so much with the jelly," Dad said.

CHAPTER 3

"Marooned three years agone," he continued, "and lived on goats since then, and berries, and oysters. Whatever a man is, says I, a man can do for himself. But, mate, my heart is sore for Christian diet. You mightn't happen to have a piece of cheese about you, now?"

Treasure Island, Robert Louis Stevenson

In Martial Arts, speed is not the true way. As far as speed is concerned, the question of fast or slow in anything comes from failure to harmonize with the rhythm.

The Book of Five Rings, Miyamoto Musashi

From my blue notebook:

Gross Joe woke up at 4 a.m. and took a long piss. He had a nightmare about the Indian chief dancing around under his window in the moonlight again. He pissed long and hard into the toilet bowl, felt a sense of relief, and forgot the ghost nonsense. What the hell was he, a kid anyway?

Joe let out a fart that made the dog leave the room, then tried to go back to sleep. What the hell was wrong with him, having nightmares like a little kid?

* * *

The aluminum canoe was painted camouflage, a great little set-up for a duck hunter. The gunwales were low and a brace bar in the middle seemed to keep everything together. The seats were low in the boat and spot welded in not so much perfection. Eventually Richard gave it to Dad in exchange for legal advice and it became a blessing to the family, and still is to this day.

We pushed off into the river with our small supplies of goods that included lunch, a couple of paddles, cushioned seats that float, a 35 millimeter camera and a .22 pistol with some ammo. The boat was slick from the light drizzle but the day was touched with a growing, dry breeze that promised good weather.

Beams of sunlight filtered through the canopy of trees as we glided by the shoreline. The smell of pine, oak, and elm permeated the wet river air, the Dutch elm disease had not yet killed all the elm trees and their aroma made a perfume that mixed with the smell of the living moss nearby.

The mighty Wisconsin River is one of the hardest working rivers in the world with many dams on it. The way to Brokaw is twenty miles by highway—a straight shot but the river serpentines on its way and makes for a longer trip. If rain levels have been low, paddlers have to get out of their canoe and push it over the rocky bottom of the riverbed.

The paddlers must take off their shoes and socks, unless they want wet feet for the day, then step on the slippery smooth stones in the river and guide the empty boat to deeper water. Crayfish might dart about. The cool water refreshes hot feet while paddlers drag the boat over the rocks and sand on the river bottom.

The river was low that day. The sun came out and was shining on us in the morning. We paddled gently and made each other laugh—something we had grown good at. We didn't think to ask ourselves if there had been enough rain to lift the river—we didn't think that way.

I sat in the back and powered the boat with my strokes and then hung the wood blade in the water steering it, like a ruder. I called out a cadence for a while and pointed out pretty birds or a weasel I had seen on the shoreline. I felt like an eleven-year-old Scout leader.

As the morning turned into afternoon and the journey lasted longer than we planned, we got tired. Keeping posture in a canoe for an extended period of time can be a challenge if not accustomed to it.

We pulled up to the river bank when we saw a picnic table on a nice piece of mowed grass. Dad and I stopped and ate our lunches: peanut-butter-and-jelly sandwiches, an apple, and a can of sun-warmed Coke.

When we settled into an eating silence, I noticed the blue depression settling on Dad. We had stopped moving, and in resting, his mind was reviewing his life again. We didn't get in the canoe fast enough. When I pushed us off from the shoreline and steadied myself on the narrow stern of the canoe and sent us out into the gentle current stream, Dad's shoulders had dropped and now he stooped in the seat at the front of the boat. He was looking down into the water, rather than out and around us.

"Fifteen men and a dead man's chest!" I called out and waited for Dad to answer in the ' Yo Ho Ho and a bottle of rum.' He didn't.

I imagined a camera shot, high angle, from a helicopter rolling down the river, with the sound of drums. It would pick up the image of our canoe, roll past us and show a horde of dead zombie Indians with tomahawks waiting for us in the river, just around the bend. The living cadavers waded out or crouched on the bank, waiting for our approach with the hatred of white man shared by so many today.

Dad's paddle lay across the gunwales. The wooden blade dripped a steady stream of droplets into the brown water, but then they tapered off.

"Current? We don't need no stinking current," I said in my *Blazing Saddles* voice. Dad didn't respond. But we did need current; the river bottom had started scraping on our aluminum bottom. From the back of the canoe, I directed us with the blade of my paddle. We slipped around the corners of the river and I kept us in the thick of the moving water as best as I could. But it happened as I knew it would, the camouflaged canoe grated on the rocky bottom of the river and we ground to a halt.

The sun beat down on us. My legs felt like skillet handles and the thick mop of black hair on my head felt like a coonskin cap.

We had to get out and pull the boat over the shallow areas. This sent Dad into a spiral of despair. "What is this, the endless voyage? How long is this trip?"

"Not much further," I said, having no idea if it were true. Once we were back in, I paddled toward what I thought were the deeper parts, but could only dip part of the blade of the paddle before touching bottom.

Hours passed and the sun shone on our heads. We passed by the freeway overpass that indicated we were only a short stretch of distance from Merrill.

"Man, what the hell is this—a canoe trip or a career move," Dad exclaimed. "What the hell have we got ourselves in for? I didn't sign on for a week-long retreat to hell."

"It's not a career move, or you wouldn't have anything to do with it." I couldn't resist. I waited in the critical moment to see if he would topple the positive way and laugh his ass off at my comment, or get super pissed at me.

"You too, huh, kid?" And then his ears turned red. "I get shit like that from everyone around me and now I have to hear it from you, too?"

"Come on, I'm sorry. I was trying to get you to laugh."

"Yeah? Well do me a favor and don't do me any favors."

I pulled on the paddle to get us over a swirl that I hoped didn't have a rock under it. It did and we hit the rock slightly sideways. It grabbed the edge of our boat and held it while the current pushed us into the downward motion of the river. The port-side edge tipped down and the starboard side rose up past my shoulder.

We dumped into the two-foot-deep water in a slow spill. I stood up quickly and grabbed at the items around me. The important items—the weapon was in a holster on my belt and I retrieved my paddle and seat cushion. The camera was gone.

Dad got to his feet with a look of shocked fury on his face. I moved toward the upended canoe that was filling with water. I dragged it to the side of the river and pulled up on the front end and turned it on its side, trying to empty the water.

"Find your paddle," I called out to him. He was standing in the knee-deep water, feeling his pockets in a mild panic.

"My cigarettes got wet." He said it like he was announcing no oxygen in a space capsule. I saw his paddle floating down the stream ahead of us.

We got the boat upright. Water was in the bottom and nothing could be done about that until we got to shore. We shoved the aluminum camouflage raider back into the eddy stream and I paddled hard while I still had my eye on Dad's escaped floating, wood paddle. Several times as I got close to coming up on it, the current carried it away.

Dad couldn't give a damn about the paddle.

"This just goes on and on," he said. "Each time we round a bend I think the boat landing is going to be there. It turns out to be another false peak. I'm sitting here in this fucking boat with a pair of soaked balls and three dry cigarettes for how long? What the hell is this, a bad acid trip?" Dad said throwing his hands up.

I finally got the boat near the vital escaped object.

"Grab that paddle, will ya?" I said. Dad leaned over and snatched it out of the water like it was inconsequential and then he rested it on the gunwales. I heard his Zippo snap and smelled the aroma of lighter fluid and expelled tobacco. A cloud of smoke puffed around his head before being snatched by the wind.

"I've had it with this shit. Everything I try to do just fails. I can't get a break, no matter what. I just don't have it in me. I give up. I give up on life, give up on everything. Fuck it."

I kept paddling. On the east side of the river I saw swirling current with the delicious maple sugar looking foam and I moved us over to it.

"Don't worry about it, I got it." I didn't know why I said that. He clearly wasn't worried about it. The chore was just paddling anyway, not like it was hard. And it was a nice day, and I was with my dad. I was just happy to be there. The afternoon did drone on, but Dad realized there was nowhere to go and nothing he could do about the situation, so he positioned himself in a state of shut-down.

After cornering yet another bend in what Dad called "the endless river," I saw what we were looking for. To make sure it was not a mirage, I looked away and glanced again at the river bank. A big lumber yard with walls of logs stacked up, ready to be moved to the mill, made a maze away from the water. We had made it to Brokaw. I felt a sense of accomplishment.

I heard drums beat in my ears. Then I imagined a camera angle, coming up the river like a swooping bird, the reflection of a helicopter visible on the water.

The camera angle passed us: rolling water, until it panned over another canoe, with dead zombie Sioux warriors in it—one with a musket taking aim at us.

"Get down! They're shooting at us!" I yelled. Dad turned to look at me. I dipped the paddle with deep hard strokes.

"What?" Dad said.

I felt my face flush.

"Nothing," I replied. I moved the paddle through the dark river water. It rolled off the surface like root beer.

Our brave, little boat grounded onto the smooth rocks of the river bank. The new freeway was visible; I looked at the passing cars. Now, to them, I was the guy getting out of a boat in a picture-perfect, outdoor-life situation. Anyone driving by would look with admiration on my situation, I hoped. I wanted to be that guy for a moment.

I stretched my back. Six hours in a canoe made me grateful to be able to stand on ground and straighten up. Things like standing can be taken for granted. A sense of accomplishment settled on me.

We pulled the boat up so it wouldn't float away.

"Come on, we have to find a phone to call Richard."

Dad was in charge again. He set off while I was still urinating. My yellow fluid streamed out into the river and made me one with it somehow. I was a part of the river now. My contribution registered, no matter how miniscule.

We walked through a massive lumber-yard-maze of logged trees that stood in well-organized stacks, like building-high barricades. The dirt under our feet was rich and turned up from heavy trucks. The air smelled thick with creosote and pine in the heat.

Brokaw is a paper mill town just north of Wausau. The town is inhabited by the employees of the paper mill. No one could buy a house here unless you worked for the paper mill. It feels like stepping onto a movie set as you walk down the streets. The stop signs look like movie props and the houses look like one-dimensional images made of cardboard, supported with boards that lean up against them with nothing behind them.

The sidewalk was as clean as a church floor and our footfalls echoed off the brick houses with the lawns mowed to exact specs. I looked again at the grass in front of the houses. I wondered how the people of the town could have cut their lawn on the same day to have it the same length in every front yard we walked by.

"Something isn't right," I said out loud—like they would in the movies. The music would start here, slow at first, but menacing. Dad walked on ahead of me, his stride heavy. The day was getting long.

In the windows of the houses we passed, I saw no one inside. No one crossed the street ahead of us to go into the post office. No cars drove by. I turned as we walked and looked behind us, taking a few backward steps. In the movies, this is where I would see a zombie in a storefront window eating the brains of a dead shop keeper. He would look up at me around rotting eyes and snarl.

I imagined us running from Indian zombies that came out from the houses. They smelled us as food. Dad and I would be running down the street—an eleven-year-old kid with his homeless father against all odds in this epic horror film directed by Jamie Finucan—my inside ears heard from some announcer with a little too much enthusiasm.

"Hey, kid. Did you hear me?" Dad asked.

"What?" I said and squinted into the sun to look in the direction of his face.

"I said, 'go knock on the door and ask to use the phone and call Richard Putnam's number.' He is expecting our call. Tell him we're in Brokaw and need a ride at the boat landing through the lumber yard." Dad paused. "Are you in reality now?"

"Yeah," I said, and swatted at the only fly in Brokaw that buzzed around my head.

"Where do you go when you phase out like that?" he asked me.

I turned away. My attention-span was short and if I didn't move, I knew I would forget my instructions.

"Is it a problem for you?" he asked me.

"Is what a problem for me?"

"When you take off into your own world."

"No, it's actually a blessing."

I went up to the door and pushed the button that had a little red light in the center of it. A series of chimes went off behind the door and a dog barked a few times, then stopped.

A girl of about my age, with big eyes and brown, thick hair, opened the door and smiled at me with her mouth, but not with her eyes. I asked to use the phone. She looked me over and then over my shoulder at Dad, who stood on the sidewalk smoking a cigarette. When her eyes fell back on mine, she looked like she wanted to say something, but decided not to. She let me into the house and across a clean kitchen to a big, yellow phone with a long, stretched-out cord that hung on the wall. She sat down at a Formica table and twisted her hair in her finger as I made the call.

I thanked her and made my way back to the door. She followed me. Then, as I got to the door, she twirled out the door in front of me and spun around in some kind of ballet dance.

"I go to dance lessons on Thursday night. Momma says I am the best in the class."

"Very good then," I said and smiled, moving to walk around her. She stopped and watched me walk out to Dad who was waiting on the sidewalk.

"How did it go?" Dad asked, flipping a cigarette butt into the street, possibly the only one there had ever been in history.

"Um, she goes to dance class on Thursdays," I answered.

"No, Richard. What did Richard say?"

"He is on his way."

We walked back the way we had come, winding through the log maze toward the river that I could smell. The eerie town that smelled of paper mill and industry fell away behind us. The logging yard could be a good place for a movie scene where two guys have to shoot it out, dodging behind the solid cover and using the maze in an attempt to outwit the opponent in a deadly game of "shoot-em up." I drifted off on that and wrote some dialogue that went with a shootout.

It would have to be something like, "It doesn't have to end this way, Charlie, and I just want to talk to you. Now put that gun down," one guy would yell as he reloaded his revolver. The answer would be a couple of pot shots from the other actor to say "screw you."

"Hey, did you hear me?" Dad was saying.

"No, sorry. What?" I reentered the real world.

"You were a real trooper today, Jamie, and you pulled us through," Dad said and tousled my hair with his hand. His eyes were tired and they looked a little wet.

"It was fun," I replied.

We waited by the canoe and I skipped rocks on the swirling water surface. I started playing a game in my imagination that if a rock didn't skip at least three feet between the first and second skip, a bomb would go off and kill us both. But I stopped because I didn't want to phase out again.

"I spent some time in the nut house, which was hard," Dad said in a tired voice. "They give you these drugs, like Thorazine; you feel like you're stuck to the ceiling. But for a while, your head doesn't bother you—when it is sedated to a maximum level." The image of my dad in an insane asylum stopped my arm from throwing the rock.

"I slept in the doorway of a church in Kansas City when I ran out of bus fare. Who the hell locks the door of a church? If the poor people can't climb in a church and stay warm, where the hell can anyone go?"

"I don't know," I answered.

We were back at the canoe, and the Wisconsin River rolled by us like a gentle, healing river of ionic energy.

"I've wandered around this country with a disturbed restlessness, feeling like I didn't belong anywhere and nowhere was the right place for me. You sit down somewhere and feel like you need to urgently be someplace else. I get no peace wherever I go. And all the time I think of you kids and wish I was with you.

"Don't ever get a divorce, kid. It's a nightmare. Do you hear me?"

"Yes," I replied, then skipped a rock over the shifting water surface. It hit one, two, three, and then four times on the river surface before it went under. It was a new record for me.

"Who could have imagined that I would lead this type of life? Can you just imagine?" Dad said softly. The day had been long and hard, and his defenses were down. I sensed an attack of depression coming on in him.

"I'm getting that floaty feeling again," Dad said and looked for something to clutch. "It's been coming on all day."

"How long will it take for Richard to get here?" I asked.

"Maybe thirty minutes."

I went to the canoe and pulled it up a bit higher on the rocky shore line, looking for some activity that we could transfer energy to, before it was too late. There was nothing to do but wait beside the steady flow of water.

"When your mother came to me with the divorce papers, I begged her not to go through with it. I told her I would never drink again; and look, I haven't—been dry three years now. And I will never touch it again."

"Oh, you know what? When the boat turned over, we lost that nifty, little thermos with the coffee, and my camera," I said. I had to get him to stop licking the wound. I felt my own wound when I thought of the pictures I had lost on the camera.

"If she would have just hung with me, we could have stuck it out; we could have made it work. I remember the moment I fell in love with her. We had just had dinner in Madison. I was studying to get my law degree, and she turned to wave. She smiled, the moon light caught her hair, and I fell for her, right there. I lost my heart. I was never the same."

I picked up a rock the size of three of my knuckles and threw it into the river. The swirling, dark water absorbed it, like it was never there. I imagined it landing on the bottom of the river next to the others that had been dragged by glaciers. My rock would be the new guy now.

I looked for another rock. A crow cawed from a nearby treetop and I stopped to look up at it.

"Once that happens," Dad continued, "it never dies or goes away—no matter what happens. That is what love is. You can't turn it off."

It had been a long day for us both and I remember feeling that the mushy stuff needed to be confronted by the truth if we were to get to the laughs again. I remember feeling that no matter what, we should shoot each other straight and speak what we knew to be true. You can be a kid and know this in your heart as fast as any adult.

"Yeah, well, you might as well, because it is over," I said. I went to get the gear that was still in the canoe and found the cloth-covered canteen that Dad insisted we bring. I took a long drink of the cool water. It slid down my throat and poured like oil over my insides—its effect immediately refreshing and restorative to me to the bone of my soul. I had not realized how dehydrated I was.

"AHHAHH," I said, letting out a deep breath.

I took another long drink. The cool shock wave spread from my gullet out to my appendages and eased a headache I had ignored, like only a kid can.

"It's never over," Dad admonished. "This is unfinished business. You just don't close a book on it."

"The book is closed. It's time to move on," I said and offered him the canteen. He looked let down.

The popping of gravel-on-tires came to our ears and the brown, Ford, pickup truck of Richard Putnam came around the corner. Richard had a kind way of not taking Dad too seriously, and it was good medicine for situations like this.

He stepped out of his truck wearing jeans, a snap-up, western shirt, and cowboy boots. He had a big smile stretched across his handsome mug. It was never far from his face. He was a salesman and a likeable guy, and his comic relief was always welcome by both Dad and me. Richard was funny. He entered a situation with a smile, and this skill could make someone indispensable.

"Hey, Wild Counselor!" he called in his western-style greeting.

CHAPTER 4

"If you have enough Irish in you, it will kill off any other genetic part."
Pat Finucan

"When you are having a problem with someone, just look at that person with love, and feel so much love for them that it just radiates from you."
Mom

From my blue notebook:

Gross Joe caught the guy's hand as he reached for his pistol. It fired, pointing down at the sidewalk, and the bullet ricocheted away with a zinging sound. Joe kneed him hard in the groin, feeling the pelvic bone give way, and then Joe head-butted him. The Arab went down fast, hard to the concrete.

Joe moved quickly toward the full elevator as the doors closed. He crowded himself in so the steel doors closed in front of his nose. The mirrored doors showed he was stuffed in a tight box with fifteen men and ladies dressed up nice. Joe looked at himself in the mirror and smiled. He knew himself too well to try to resist. Then he let out a four-second fart that heated the ass of his pants, then his pant legs, and then over his leather shoes. The pungent vapor rose like the invisible results of a broken fog machine on a dance floor.

It stayed low at first. but then rose up around everyone like poison mustard gas in a trench. A few tried to hold their breath, but it was a long way to the fourth floor.

Joe let out his diabolical laughter, the one that sounded like the bad guys in the movies.

* * *

A new construction site was in full swing on a lot by the park. John and I, with our dirt bikes, were climbing up a mound of freshly-lifted earth that had been delivered but left unattended on a sweet Sunday. The incline was steep and the tires sunk into the soft dirt too far before we could reach the top. We pedaled the bikes up the hill until they couldn't go further, then rode the tumble back down.

I looked over at the other mound of dirt and saw two kids, close to our age, standing on the dirt. I hadn't seen them approaching. They had appeared like specters, staring hatefully at us.

Spit was tall and lean, and Klosuski was a wrestler who had matched and even beat me once in practice. He always had a scowl on his mug and a hateful squint in his eyes.

They stood on the opposite mound, waiting for us to notice them.

"Hey, it's Spit and Ski," said John. He dropped his bike and stood up. "I owe that fucker Spit from the last baseball game, when he jacked me in the face in the dugout and then ran behind his big brother."

When I looked over at them, I saw he was right. Spit wore his maw in scowl. Klosuski put his hands together and started cracking his knuckles. The popping sound was eerily loud, reaching us across the dirt mound chasm. Ski had punched Joey Barnes in the face at the fireworks last year. Everybody was a tough guy.

For several moments the four of us were silent, starring at each other. Each team stood on its opposing mounds of dirt while we stared at each other in aggressive loathing. There was something healthy in this moment. I knew who I was, and who was on my side in that moment, an old friend beside me that I could count on. I never would have guessed that later in life, that self-aware sensation would be so rare.

There was an anger that lit in me and always would be there to kindle. A target for the frustration in life, a recipient of channeled revolt against the stacked deck of destiny, a way to register an objection was at hand. I understood that—like my brother, Tim, did.

We broke at the same time. John and I dropped down and grabbed dirt clods; some with rocks—we didn't care—and started throwing them at the two goons.

Clearly, the time for confrontation had come. It happened sometimes without prelude: an aggressive game of king-of-the-mountain in the winter just happened in an instant on a snow bank by a plowed parking lot. Or, in the summer, a few kids from a nearby beach gathered to a silent summons for a game of king-of-the-raft, like retired guys to a poker game in a back room. There were times of challenge and acceptance of that challenge. This was one of them.

Taking us on was a mistake because, while I could throw with power and get distance, I had no accuracy. John Purcell, on the other hand, could throw anything as fast as a lightning bolt with uncanny precision.

He was the pitcher of our championship little-league team, the Pirates. We had won the division that spring, in spite of the fact that his mother was the coach. His arm was like a bowstring—when something left his hand it was an arrow that didn't miss.

Once I saw him nail a cocky kid with a snowball from seventy yards away. He arched it up into the air, stepped into it, his winter jacket making a cracking sound at the release. It left his hand destined for the target. The trajectory was perfect for intersection on the moving figure.

The snowball seemed to vaporize into a fine powder as it hit the kid's head. He collapsed like a lung on a broken rib when the ice ball smashed into his face from a perfect arc of interception, leaving the kid withering on the school playground.

"No hard feelings," John had yelled afterward with a shrug.

Now, John was popping up and drilling clods into both Spit and Ski when they surfaced to throw. He had them pinned down. Cries of agony after the sound of a rock or dirt clod striking scalp came to us in our cover and we laughed as we threw.

A dirt clod hit my face and spattered dirt from my nose across my cheek. I hit the ground hard. I touched my face and saw blood on my hand. John kept up the aggression until they had had enough. Due to taking too many hits or becoming bored, they abandoned their position and wandered off, away from the hill.

Spit turned and yelled at me.

"Hey, Finucie, Krumel is looking for you, and oh, does he have an ass kicking for you!" he yelled with unmistakable glee in his voice. "You can't hide forever."

"I ain't hiding from anybody, you turd," I yelled back. My nose was bleeding and my ears had a ringing in them from the rock that hit me in the face.

When I looked in their direction again, they were gone.

The town seemed big and we ran the distance to the bowling alley, where John's Grandma Ruthie was a championship bowler. With a few bucks, we played arcade games like Pac Man and Frogger. We raced cars on a screen in front of us while we actually got to sit in a driver's seat. During the school year, we were on a bowling league called the Pinball Wizards that took third that year in the bowl off. There was a girl in school who made some wizard costumes but we never had the balls to wear them. And besides, who wants to bowl in a stupid robe and a pointed hat with a star on it?

When we had spent most of the few bucks we had, we climbed on the bars outside that held up the overhang of the roof. It started to rain but the overhang kept us dry.

John went back into the lanes and I walked over to the bait shop. I purchased a Chang Chi Master of Kung Fu comic book, some fishing line, and big stick of Laffy Taffy. After I paid, I stood out under the overhang and pulled off a big, stretch yank of the taffy.

My mouth flooded with saliva as I worked on the sour candy. I started reading the comic book and marveled at how Chang Chi was kicking the crap out of assholes that had it coming, when I heard the hiss of brakes on the street.

The Greyhound Bus pulled up and belched out diesel smoke. The door opened with a flopping sound. A girl of about my age got off the bus and looked around. The driver came off the bus and opened the under-carriage door. The girl was cute—black haired with an olive touch to her skin. The driver walked around and took out a brown, stuffed suitcase from the baggage under-stow and put it down next to her. She stood there in the rain as the bus pulled away.

The black smoke couldn't cover how cute she was. She was athletic in build with thick, raven-black hair. Her big, brown eyes flashed around in vulnerability. She looked like she was scared and confused, but was fighting it.

I watched her through the dribbling water off the roof of the bait shop, and when she began to cry, my heart went right out to her.

I took one more bite of the taffy, then wrapped it up in the paper and stuffed it in my front pocket with the fishing line. Then I folded the comic book like the blue notebook and slid it into my back pocket. I stepped out from the cover and walked over her way, pretending that I hadn't seen her arrive.

I didn't know what else to do, so I stood next to her like I was waiting for a bus.

"Nice day," I commented to her. She sniffled. "...if you happen to be a duck." She looked away from me to hide the tears.

"Something wrong?" I asked.

"I'm supposed to meet my daddy here. He must have forgotten that I was getting here today." A tear ran from the outside of her eye and she caught it expertly with her fingertips.

"Or his car broke down or something," I countered. "This town is so small you can walk anywhere in a few minutes. Where are you going?"

She showed me the address.

"That's not far from my house. It's only a few blocks. I'll show you. Let me take that suitcase," I said and hefted it. "Cheeze, what do you have in here, cement?" I made a show of having to struggle to lift it. Her big, dark eyes smiled over her bee-stung lips and she laughed nervously, but genuinely. That was all I was going for.

The era of duffel bags with shoulder straps had not yet arrived. The case had a hard top that was a struggle to carry for the next mile-and-a-half of streets. The rain was falling lightly but enough so that we were both soaking wet. I watched her appearance change in the rain. As her hair matted down around her head, she seemed to be a different girl.

In the smell of the rain I caught lavender, some kind of perfume she was wearing. I told her stories about town and my friends, and tried to make her feel comfortable. I didn't want to see her cry anymore.

When we finally arrived at her house, I staggered in surprise. The house had roof-shingle siding, the paint had chipped off around the windows, and the porch hung at a crooked angle on the front of the house.

Derik Lawton's yellow pickup truck was in the driveway. Gus's scratch was still fresh down the driver's door. I smiled at the dog's retribution; Gus knew how to handle humans that acted like assholes.

"What did you say your name was?" I asked.

"Trish Lawton," she said with a smile.

"Jamie Finucan."

"Thanks for your help." She moved over and kissed my cheek. I reeled. I watched her go into the battered front door, her beauty in contrast to the unkept building. I walked home breaking out into dance numbers along the way, a few attempts at tap dancing, then a spinning side-kick with part of a kata I learned. After a few paces to catch my breath, I retreated into my imagination of chivalrous fantasy of bravado—in my own world, where I lived so often and could spend hours back then. Just as I approached my house, the wind picked up and the rain came down sideways like little stinging darts from a million blow guns.

* * *

That night Derik Lawton tried to kill my dad at the Richard Putnam farm house. Dad was watching television while on Richard's couch, enjoying a reprieve from being homeless for an evening. He was watching Johnny Carson do his monologue when gunfire poured in through the French door windows that faced him, behind the television set.

The glass in the doors fell and the couch he was sitting in took bullets to the left of him and tracked fast toward Dad. Dad was a former Marine and dove to the floor, then rolled across the room the instant it began.

The bullets poured in from the dark night, tracking him across the sofa and across the room as he rolled toward the wall. They stopped when he hit the wall. Dad kept moving and got to his backpack and found his Browning Hi Power 9mm pistol. He went outside and moved along the side of the house slowly.

He saw footprints in front of the window and a few .22 casings in the grass, but the shooter was gone. Dad went in and called the Lincoln County Sheriff's department and they came out and took a report. The made a plaster cast of a boot print in the dirt and asked Dad some questions about who would want to hurt him.

That was it. They didn't look too hard for the perpetrator, never followed up with him, and never had a suspect.

"That's what happens when you're poor. No one gives a damn about you. Do you think if I was a big shot in this town I would get this treatment?" he would say later that summer.

I heard about it the next day when he stood there in mom's kitchen wearing his Marines T-shirt. He was furious. His Browning pistol would be close at hand from now on in his small grip of gear that contained all the stuff he had in the world.

The injustice of it stuck in my gut. Every degenerate shithead seemed to have it out for us. The world seemed to be full of hard-ons with something to prove against the Finucans. I thought of Erik Krumel and how he was looking for me, telling anyone who he thought knew me that he was looking for me. He beat up my friends and sought to injure someone everywhere he went. I was getting sick of feeling like prey.

A man had just shot at my dad when he had landed a place to sleep for a few nights, so that he couldn't even enjoy a brief reprieve from being homeless by sleeping under a roof. And no one was going to do anything about it.

In that moment the whole set-up seemed unfair to me and woke a rage within me that sometimes I still feel burning in the pit of my soul. I remember asking Dad questions about the incident and drawing out every detail that I could. In my chest I heard my breathing tremble. I got a glass of water and saw my hand shaking.

I wanted justice from this life, this town, this world. Eleven years old or not, I was going to do something about this shit.

CHAPTER 5

"If I would have known what it was like to have four kids, I would have chopped my cock off with a hatchet."
Dad, when he was mad at Tim and me

"Hey, a beer would go good with that pizza, or sorry that's your face."
Deirdre (my sister)

When you are exchanging blows with an opponent in a duel, you hit the opponent's own sword with your sword as he strikes; this is called the slapping parry.
The Book of Five Rings, Miyamoto Musashi

In my notebook, I was trying my hand at poetry and wrote:

Ditch weed
What is the name of that plant that smells so sweet and thick, only on the hottest of summer days?
In the bottom of the ditch it lays like a gas that grandpa tasted in WWI, in a trench.
It's camphoric and intoxicating, overcoming the senses, commanding notice like a warning.
It is only there in the heat.
I wish I knew its name; that would give me power over it.
Cuz then I could capture it somehow and put it in a bottle.

Then I could take it out when I wanted to sleep, or
When I wanted comfort and then I could fill my senses with it,
Drifting off to sleep then, away on a cloud of intoxication.

*   *   *

That summer I proved that the adolescent mind is not capable of projecting into the future to estimate consequences. It isn't capable; it hasn't learned enough life experiences and has not fully developed in the skill of reaction to action.

Mike lived across the street from the Chip's Hamburger stand. He had a tent pitched in his backyard and had been sleeping in it by himself a couple of nights a week. "It's hard at first—it makes your back sore but it gets easier," he said like he was summiting Everest. I thought of Dad sleeping outside all the time.

I went over to his house with some smoke bombs—the cool-looking, circular ones that were bright colors on the outside, yellow or blue—take your pick. A big thick fuse came off the top with a base of adhesive.

Whatever color the exterior of the bomb was, was the same color of voluminous smoke that poured out. I had the idea that it would be fun to light off two smoke bombs and watch the tent fill up with smoke with all the windows zipped up.

We selected a blue and yellow one. We laughed like we might be playing a joke on ourselves. We got in the tent, zipped up the small square window and the door, so no smoke could get out. Then we lit them both at the same time and sat Indian-style on the nylon floor of the tent, facing each other with the smoke bombs between us, and watched the fuses burn down.

I smelled the acid smoke of the fuse and waited. The mental light did not come on as to what we were doing until the yellow smoke erupted, pouring out thick, like a gas. Then the fuse of the blue one burned down to the bomb and it gushed out a thick, steady plume of smoke into the tent—more smoke than I can remember ever seeing come out of them.

I played the James Bond theme in my head. The villain might be saying: "Ah, Mr. Bond, are you sure there is nothing that you want to tell me before you die?"

Mike's expression changed a little as his image faded in a cascade of yellow, thick smoke. The tent filled solid. We couldn't see or breathe in a few seconds. That's when the epiphany hit us. This was a stupid idea that could get us killed, and we had to get out of here if we were to survive, if it already wasn't too late.

We scrambled for the tent door, which was already gone in the haze of yellow and now blue smoke, but we knew the direction. We clawed over each other in a frantic attempt to find the tiny zipper in the nylon tomb that had become a possible death trap. The air around us was a thick yellow mud and my eyes could only burn in my sockets rather than see anything.

The struggle ensued with fits of choking and hacking. A knee hit my head; Mike's hand was in the way of mine as I tried to follow the zipper line with my fingertips before I passed out. We were both gagging and hacking with retching sounds that threatened to tear stomach lining.

Mike got the zipper to the door open and stood up in the tent, taking in the fresh air, standing in the doorway. He didn't move over, so I had to push my way past him until I was clear of the toxic smog and then I rolled in the grass trying to inhale over collapsed lungs that spasmed and retched in revolt.

"What were we thinking?" I asked myself as I breathed the fresh, sweet air around me. There was no discussion for a few minutes. A blue jay was singing its screech and a robin was peeping, seemingly to mock us.

The narrow escape from death gave me a taste of the preciousness of life. I looked back at the smoke-engulfed tent. A fire had started inside the center of the tent from the smoke bombs having rolled over in the commotion for the unseen door.

"Get the hose! Hose that down or we'll have the fire department here with the cops," I called as I choked. Mike only retched, leaning his hands on his knees, then looking intently at the grass at something that he had thrown up.

I saw the green garden house on the side of the red house, lying next to the structure. I staggered over, spun the handle, and hit the tent with a steady stream of water that sent more smoke billowing up into the leaves of the overhead maple tree.

Then I pointed the force of the hose straight up and it produced a delicious fount of bubbling, clear essence. I drank it over my fire-hot throat.

It took us only a short time to recover; we were young. Then we moved on into the day, with no reflection on what there was to learn from such an experience. We shrugged it off, and tumbled on.

The afternoon ended with us catching frogs down by the Prairie River that ran through town. We tried to get them to race, but they were not cooperative.

"I'm going home for lunch. I would invite you over but we only have enough hot dogs and beans for Mom and me," he said and took off on his bike. I tossed the frogs like they were grenades into the water and they swam away.

* * *

I rode my bike downtown and when I passed the jail, I saw my dad walking down the street. His head was aimed down at the ground and his shoulders were stooped. His feet moved slowly in the trod of the dejected. I pulled up beside him.

"Hi, Dad. Where have you been? I haven't seen you around the past few days."

"No, you haven't because I have been in jail. I got arrested and the cops threw me in jail. That's where I have been. Didn't anyone think to look for me?"

I pushed my bike and walked beside him on the sidewalk. A sunbeam shined on us for a moment and I wanted to stop to stand in its warmth.

"I can just disappear and my own family won't look for me. What the hell kind of family do we have here?" Dad said looking at me.

"I just thought you were at Richard's house for a few days to work on his legal problems."

"Did your mother ask where I had been?"

"She did ask if you were around," I lied. That seemed to work a bit.

"That's what this town has for the poor—a jail cell. The level of oppression in this community is astounding. These aren't just cops in this town, they're members of Gestapo. What kind of town arrests vagrants and throws them in jail? It's not an actual crime now to be poor and homeless.

"I have one unpaid parking ticket, and these cops are all over it, but some psychopath cranks off ten rounds at me through a living room window and they don't have a clue how to investigate it. These moron cops don't know how to investigate a crime scene, but they're real good at locking up poor people for parking tickets. That's business as usual around here."

"What unpaid ticket?" I asked.

"Some ridiculous, unpaid, parking ticket from long ago. I haven't even had a car in two years, since I had to sell it to eat."

I pictured the 1947, International Harvester, pickup truck he had driven around for a while. He had one of Deirdre's friends paint a picture of a yin and yang symbol on the door. When I thought of Dad selling it, I pictured a cowboy shooting his horse for a meal on a snowy mountain.

"Little Brave Truck?" I asked, trying to get a smile from him by mentioning the name he had given it. The truck incident came to my mind. Dad had this incredible, little truck from an era when they overbuilt stuff. It was fantastic.

He also had gotten a dog that summer, a German Shepherd, that would keep him company and fend off the loneliness. Dad was staying at the Maybe Inn in Tomahawk and driving around with this big rambunctious dog that, on one occasion, had bitten him.

Dad had driven out to Gleason to see a client, Gordon Hanrahan, a big, thick-necked farmer who appreciated my dad's sense of humor. He had hired me to mow his lawn, but fired me the same afternoon when I mistakenly mowed a patch out of his soy bean field, thinking it was his lawn.

Before heading for Gleason, Dad put the dog in the back of the pickup and tied the leash to the truck. The dog jumped out somewhere on the drive and Dad dragged the dead dog through the town of Gleason at the posted speed limit.

He later told me, "I was wondering why all these people were staring at me. I thought 'What is it with these assholes in this town?' But when I got to the farm, I found the dog behind the truck and realized it was horror on their faces."

"Yeah, Little Brave Truck," he sighed. "You didn't even notice that I was gone?" he asked me again, throwing the glance that weighed me.

"I'm sorry, Dad. How would I have guessed that?"

"Et tu, Brute?"

"What?"

"It means 'You, too, Brutus?' It's Shakespeare. Come on, let's go to Chip's. I got some money from Father," Dad said. Sometimes the priest gave Dad ten dollars to get food. We walked to Chip's for a Blue Jay Burger.

The 70-degree temperature felt a little chilly with a breeze that picked up, and the clouds moved over the sun. We ate outside anyway. Dad was hoping for some warm rays on him since he had been in a jail cell for three days. He looked tired. The experience had drained him and would cause a massive attack of depression.

We ate in silence with the cars passing by. I knew his mentality in these moments and said things very carefully. I learned then to use a pleasant and soothing tone.

"Don't get disabled in life. Be careful of the decisions you make. Don't screw around in your marriage; there are some sins that cry out for God's vengeance. Infidelity is one of them.

"I did. And I am paying the price. My drinking and acting like an asshole cost me my whole life, and I just can't seem to recover from it."

The sun came out and touched our circular table with the bright, colored seats and warmed our skin.

"Look at me, I'm a bum."

"Why don't you get a job?" I asked gently.

"I would like to. Jerry Maeder, a famous lawyer in Wausau, saw me in a coffee shop and tried to talk to me, but I couldn't handle it, and I didn't say the right things."

"What do you mean?"

"When you're broken in your head, you suffer from a disassociation that doesn't allow you to connect to other people. The smallest interactions with other people are incredibly painful. If they come up to you and say "hi", it's a devastating experience. Can you understand that?"

"Sure," I lied.

"If it ever happens to you, and God forbid it should, there are things you can do. You can live outside, you can camp, and you can forage for food. You can sleep under the stars with nothing but a hungry belly and know that God is with you. You can survive." He looked at me across the table. "If I am able to show you this, that would give purpose to this experience and it will have reason then. But you have to learn to protect yourself. You don't know what life has in store for you.

"This experience has changed me in many ways and given me a new perspective on life and the people who don't have anything."

"So, is it good in some ways?"

"No, it sucks. People hate you everywhere you go; they treat you worse than a dog. They have no respect for you as a person. Even people you know don't want you around when there is no place for you to go to, and who could blame them?

"You become this ghost—that's what the poor are, ghosts that no one wants to see. If you do vanish for three days, no one notices. It's like you are invisible in society. Even to your own kids. It's enormously lonely. You wander around like a leper in tremendous pain and agony with no one to share it with."

"Not all the time," I said. "You and I have a lot of laughs. We have fun playing in the park and cooking out over fires. I am having a ball hanging out with you, Dad."

He almost flinched.

"Oh, I am having fun with you, too, little buddy," he responded and looked at me with new regard.

"Then let's go down to Blue Boats and go swimming," I suggested.

"It's too cold for that. The temperature needs to be warmer."

"Want to go play Frisbee in Normal Park? We can go get Gus, The Wonder Dog, to play with us."

"I would like to see Gus. Yes, let's go do that."

We stood up, crunched up the paper wrappers our charbroiled burgers had come in, and headed off for some activity. If I caught Dad's mental spiral early enough, I could deflect it away from depression. The answer was engaging in activity.

We started walking and crossed the street. I imagined a scene in a movie: a smoky cockpit of a small engine plane. A wounded co-pilot, bleeding from a gunshot hole, is pulling on the yoke of a P47. The thin metal is perforated with bullet holes from a .30 caliber. "Pull up, pull up!" the also-wounded pilot yells out over the increasing engine roar. The ground rushes up into the windshield.

"Why did you say that?" Dad asked me.

"Say what?"

"You just called out something." Dad stopped. He was looking at me, concerned.

"Oh, I was just thinking."

A car drove by with Jenny Wilson in the passenger seat. She turned her head to look at me. For a moment I was ashamed to be walking next to my homeless dad.

Then I hated myself for feeling that way.

CHAPTER 6

Run a moist pen over everything and start afresh.
Charles Dickens

Everyone falls off the bike. The winners have the balls to get back up and get back on. Then finish the race—not push the bike off the course like a candy ass.
Tim Finucan, to me, during a dirt-bike race.

From my blue notebook:
…a drawing of a man throwing up on the top of a page. The vomit ran down the margins of the page in billows of blue ink.

My brother, Tim, was four years older than me. He was lean and tall with curly hair that he hated and kept under a baseball cap. His stare was direct and his wit sharp and quick. Tim had accomplished the art of goal-setting and achievement at an executive-level of performance in anything he did—by the time he was nine. He liked to win and got straight A's in school. He also excelled in sports, like cross country, tennis, and the backyard boxing that was so popular.

When Tim was ten years old and decided he wanted a mini-bike, he picked nightcrawlers every night. On summer nights I could see him in Dr. Beyer's yard with a flashlight and an ice cream bucket with some dirt in the bottom of it.

I went out and helped him sometimes. The picking was especially good after a rain. The wet grass and the beam of my flashlight picked up their slippery tubular bodies that slithered in my fingers when grabbed. They were slimy and fast. The fat, juicy nightcrawlers moved quickly and could be down a hole in the ground faster than you think a worm could move.

Tim sold the nightcrawlers to Fred Walburger, at Fred's bait shop, and purchased a mini-bike. Tim decided what he wanted, then figured out a way to get it without excuses. He never let an obstacle stop him from his objective. He was bow hunting deer at age eleven. I remember watching him leave the house with a bow and marveling at the prospect of killing a deer with this stick and some string.

My oldest brother, Shawn, had a big, heavy punching bag made of leather, with the words Everlast in a yellow label stitched on it, right about where the face would be when it hung. We all worked the bag with gloves on—frequently.

When someone was working the bag, the house rocked. The floor creaked and groaned. The chains that fastened the bag to the basement ceiling rattled. The impact, and the result, all came together in a continuous crescendo of training sounds.

Hearing one of my brothers hammering away at the heavy bag was inspiring. It was the stone that we three boys used to sharpen our inner steel for the world. The Finucan boys were preparing for war, and rocking of the bag was a tribal drum beat.

I heard Tim working the bag and I went down to watch him. He was moving toward it with his head high but his chin down, in good form, pounding away at it with his hands. His hands shot out into the leather and back to his face to cover up. His elbows were in, to protect his ribs. His feet moved lightly and he pivoted on the toes with each right he threw.

The bag seemed to double up as he worked it. His sweatshirt was soaked with sweat and the look in his eye was rage.

By looking at him in a moment, I knew what he was feeling, but not why. Rather than say anything, I watched him work it out on the bag.

"Dad came up to me today when I was with my friends and said a bunch of stupid shit and embarrassed me," said Tim. "You know how he gets when he wants to fit in, but doesn't know how, so he gets zany and flakey?"

He glanced at me and I nodded. Tim hit the bag a few more times, making an ssst sound with his mouth each time to tighten up. "Breathing Dragon," the technique was called in the martial arts world.

"There is a pretty girl at school that I would like to date. Her dad won't let her go out with me because Dad is homeless." He pounded the bag some more. "Some people are nice. Mr. Weix is always kind to me and treats me like anyone, but some of the others look at me like I was scum."

The smell of sweat and basement dryer lint hung in the air.

"I'm sick of getting shit from people because Dad is wandering around town instead of working, so I have been taking on all comers. I kicked the shit out of someone in the parking lot of McDonald's yesterday."

"About Dad?" I asked.

"No, it was in Wausau and I was wearing my Merrill sweats. This car pulls up with a few guys in it and one of them yells out the window: 'Merrill sucks.' So I said, 'So do you.' He got out of the car and walked real fast toward me. Just before he was going to swing, I stepped in and did this." He demonstrated a flurry of punches to the head and ended with a dig to the body.

"He collapsed like a punctured bladder. He had two friends who got out of the car, but neither of those pussies was having any. They stood there watching their buddy get up off the parking lot, using his hands to find his balance. It was kind of funny and awkward at the same time. I told his buddies that just stood there and watched that they were smarter than they looked." He worked the bag more; the steam seemed to be subsiding. Tim let the bag swing, then took the gloves off and started unwrapping the cloth strips from his hands.

"All those years we lived on the lake, he never had time for me, never took me fishing. Now he wants to hang out when I am with my friends and he is wearing freaky clothes with holes in them and walking around town like a lost dog. Why does he have to do that in this town? Why can't he pull that shit somewhere else?" He looked at me not wanting an answer. That was good because answers were something I was in short supply of.

"I am going to graduate from school and leave this fucking town and never look back," he said and tossed the sweat-soaked, cotton handwraps at the shelf where we kept them.

* * *

Summertime was like a big, three-month-long weekend. And when one of the three channels had a horror movie fest on, it signaled a time to invite a friend over to stay the night, watch horror movies, and eat popcorn. *Night of the Living Dead*, the classic, was going to be on and I recognized the chilling genre of the zombie movie long before it later became so popular.

Nothing was creepier than a zombie, and the original *Night of the Living Dead* was filmed in black-and-white, giving it a documentary feel.

So, Kyle and I fell asleep on the couches of the living room with the TV showing Vincent Price as the diabolical Dr. Phibes. At 1:45 a.m., we woke up to a confrontation in the breezeway of the front door. My sister Deirdre was being brought home by a policeman, a hulking mass in blue uniform. But she was up in his face.

"Get your hands off me, you puke," she said and shook loose of him. My mom entered the scene and began asking questions.

"Your daughter was found drunk at the park with some unsightly characters," the cop said.

"The only one unsightly in the park was you. Don't forget that you work for our tax dollars, which should be enough reason for you not to act like a prick. Only an asshole would roust kids for no reason. We have a right to be here. This might surprise you but even young people have a right to exist. Did you forget that this is a country of citizens, not peasants?" she yelled. "As a kid, did you beat up kids for their lunch money?"

"I will thank you to watch your tongue, young lady," the cop replied.

"You acted like an asshole at the park. You pushed around my friends and accused them of smoking pot. Do you have to work so hard at being a prick or does it come naturally for you?" She was drunk and furious.

I recognized the rage in her, too.

"That's my job," the cop said, then looked like he had been tricked into saying it.

"Deirdre, now stop it," Mom said, then turned to the cop, "and thank you for bringing her home."

"Don't thank him for being a dickhead. He could have left us alone. No one needed him tonight."

The cop turned to go out the door. He looked stunned.

"You know, no one has ever talked to me the way you have tonight," he said and looked back at us.

"Well, it's about time someone did. Maybe now you can have an idea about how to behave. Maybe now you can consider how to help people instead of shove them around like a schoolyard bully," Deirdre yelled.

"Wow," my friend Kyle said. He looked like he had seen a magic trick. The event ended with my sister stumbling off to bed and my mom shaking her head.

"Your house is wild," Kyle said.

* * *

In the early morning, I made the rounds of Merrill on my bike looking for Dad. At the library I saw Trish Lawton standing in the parking lot. I stopped to talk to her. Her smile faded when she saw me notice her black eye.

"What happened?" I asked.

"I walked into a door." She said it like "silly me," but it didn't have the ring of truth to it. I didn't know what to say. I didn't have to wait long. Derik pulled up fast in his yellow pickup truck and glared at me.

"See ya," she said and stepped up into the pickup. I slowly pedaled my bike away.

I wondered what it would be like to have some kind of special power like a comic book hero. Then perhaps I could influence the world and stand up to all the assholes in it.

I went to Riverside Park and took a small trail that went off the main part. I accelerated when I saw a mound of the army blanket on the ground. I rode my bike toward it, knowing it was Dad. No one else camped out in the city park.

"Hi, Dad," I called as I approached. He stirred from a fetal position and sat up a bit, pushing himself from the ground with his hand.

"Hi, Jamie."

His eyes opened wide in the pity mode.

"I brought you a sandwich." I handed him the peanut butter and bacon on toasted whole-wheat I had made that morning.

"Oh, well, thanks," he said taking it from me as though he didn't know what to do with it. After he sat up and looked around he opened the plastic wrap. His expression was despondent. I looked at the water of the Wisconsin River rolling past. A book with a black cover lay on the ground next to him.

"What are you reading?"

"*Black Elk Speaks*. He was a very wise medicine man," Dad said slowly. Silence seemed to surround our conversation, choking it out like a weed.

"Was he a mighty warrior?"

"He was not so much a warrior but a prophet, perhaps, to the Native American. The Indians sure got the short end of the stick from the white man," Dad said. He was identifying with their plight.

"Is that right?"

More silence rolled past us like the brown waters of the river.

"Sometimes I think about going to an Indian reservation and being an attorney. I could help them, I think," he said from far away in his own mind. I stretched out on the cool grass and looked up at the blue morning sky.

"You help a lot of people."

Dad shrugged his shoulders and tipped his head. He chewed on the sandwich with no appetite.

"Should I see if I can find us a ride to Eau Claire Dells?" I asked.

"Nah. I don't feel like doing that now."

Robins called out from an elm tree near us. A car went by with Johnnie Rivers singing "Swaying to the Music" playing out the window.

"They are tearing down Ron Priebe's house and building a Hardee's there," I said, trying to keep the conversation going.

Ron Preibe was a lawyer in Merrill who killed his young girlfriend by beating her to death with a fire poker while drunk. The girl had a little baby that became orphaned. The murder had shocked the little town.

"Tearing down that house is for the best," Dad answered. "It would be a good thing for this town to forget that it happened. I don't know what the hell he was thinking. I think he was possessed by a demon. I was in his office for a business meeting and I swear I could smell brimstone."

"What's that?"

"It's a stone that is associated with Hell. It's really what we call sulfur today. But it was so strong, I had to get out of there. It was creepy."

The sandwich was done and he was feeling energized from the food. The blood sugars in the human body responded and restored energy to the body.

"Krumel is back in town," I said.

The birds seemed to stop chirping and Dad looked at me.

"What is he doing out of the detention center?"

"He did his time, I guess."

"They turned that violent psychopath out on the street?"

"They did. And he's looking for me."

I knew I could tell Dad anything. He was my partner for taking on any problem.

"Why is he looking for you?"

"He wants to fight. He's kicking the crap out of people all over town and telling 'em, when they're on the ground, that I was next and to pass it on to me."

"Well, you don't have to knock down every asshole that comes your way, Jamie. You would be knocking down assholes all day long. You don't have to run the risk of confrontation with this guy. We'll call the cops, call his parents, and I will stick a knife in the gut of this asshole if I have to. And I will tell him that."

Dad was getting pissed.

"I'm going to call his dad. The minute I get to a phone, I'm calling the Krumel household for a little chat. Maybe I'll just go over there right now. Where does he live?"

The laws on bullying were not what they are today, and he and I knew that there was little to be done to avoid a confrontation with someone who was looking for you. I had been a Finucan long enough to know that there was a scrap waiting for me once a week around any corner. And Erik Krumel was going to be one of them.

"This is one of those things that I have to handle on my own," I said.

"No, you don't have to handle this on your own. You have a family. We handle this together. I will put the word out that I am looking for this freak. I will break his jaw with that sap."

The sap was a nifty spring of about ten inches with a lead weight at the end of it, wrapped in a black leather strip. I was unaware of a time when he ever hurt anybody.

This was one of the times I had presented him a problem and he rushed to my assistance, in whatever way he could, even if there was nothing that he could do. He would do that countless times through my life until he died. My dad was champion of my life.

"How was the sandwich?"

"It was good. Thank you for thinking of me and bringing it down here."

"It's okay. I bet I know what would go well now—a nice cup of coffee from the gas station across from the hospital."

"Yeah, that would be great. Will you go get us two of them?"

"No, you come with me. Come on, you have been lying here all morning. The day is getting on. Let's move."

Dad stood up with me, slowly, stretching his legs and looking around. He was coming around. But we had to start walking right away.

I had figured out early in life that one way to combat depression is to get off your dead ass and on your dying feet. We walked on the trail that ran beside the river, along the base of the haunted hill, chatting. The tree overhead wrapped us in shadows and a cooling load of air wafted down on us in an odor of elm and oak with a whisper of pine. He did a fake karate chop at my neck and I responded with a quick flurry of my own kung fu move.

That got him chuckling. As we walked past the hill, I could have sworn I saw an Indian medicine man step out between two trees. He held a tomahawk in one hand and, in the other, the head of one of the first owners of the mansion. When I turned my head, it had vanished. I saw only an empty park with the big, gentle river rolling past in an ionic slither of serenity.

CHAPTER 7

I love writing. I never feel really comfortable unless I am either actually writing or have a story going. I could not stop writing.
P.G. Wodehouse

Aristotle said melancholy men of all others are most witty.
Robert Burton

In the heat of the summer one morning, with my house being centrally located, my friends began to assemble. They rode their bikes from all directions of town and we waited a short time, joking, laughing and drinking in life without knowing how sweet it's nectar was. Inside we knew that this was one of the only remaining days of our childhood that were ours. Each of us had survived enough severe winters in Wisconsin, endured the seemingly endless school months to know how life presented summer in limited doses of time. Summer was like the display of a single firework: pop, magnificent, then over. And somewhere inside us, and it went unspoken, we could feel or our biochemistry was changing already. We knew for this time only, maybe just for this day, we were kids.

The summer meant swimming, and with two main rivers—the Wisconsin and the Prairie—running through and around town, there were plenty of swimming holes to blow off steam on a hot day, when we had nothing to do but play.

One of our favorite bridges for jumping off was on highway 51 behind Dick's Riverside Supper Club. The highway was busy, so we had to walk close to the rail of the narrow crossing and the drivers didn't like it. The horns beeped; the cops were called so that we knew we didn't have much time.

The water was deep. If we jumped into the middle of the river, we wouldn't hit any obstacle under water, so we dove or cannon-balled. Robbie Grefe had a good can opener. He could somehow spring up off the bridge rail and fold up one leg, holding it up against his chest and extended the other. But as he hung there in the air like a half moon, he leaned back. In that moment, when he was moving again, finally toward the water, he did look like a flipped-open, cheap can opener.

When he hit the water, Robbie sent a deluge of water over the railing and onto the passing cars' windshields and, if they had the window open, they were soaking their balls in Prairie River water.

When the police came to correct our behavior, we swam under the bridge and hung by our hands from the rafters of the bridge. Our upper bodies out of the water, we hung there and waited for the cop to grow tired of the charade and then leave. My body weight was lighter suspended in the water and the gritty feel of the iron beam overhead vibrated when the cars drove over us.

"I know you guys are under the bridge and I know you can hear me. If I drive by here in five minutes all you kids better be gone. You got me?" he called down. After he left, we took five minutes to dry off. I saw an AMC Hornet coming with the window open, so I decided on one more can opener to see if I could top Robbie's.

Ronnie Kleineschmidt approached us. He flipped his thick black hair to the side.

"Ronnie! Where you been?" I asked, then did a double-take when I saw his eye. It bared a magnificent shiner. I had seen shiners before. Some were little mouse's with just a dark swath under the afflicted eye. Some were walnuts that stuck out with inflamed trauma. His shiner was swollen on the bottom and the top, closing off the eye completely. He smiled, but looked at me with one peeper, like a cat with distemper.

Ronnie was a nice kid who was no scrapper. Whoever gave him the shiner was puke.

Committed to my attack, I jumped from the bridge and took the position of the can opener. I tucked up one knee and clutched it tight against my chest, the other leg I extended to act like a beaver tail slapping the water hard, I hoped. I felt the vortex of plunge beneath me and crashed down into the water until I was suspended in the flowing river, gently carrying me down and away.

I was awash in the weightlessness of summer and the bliss of no responsibilities. I was a kid on the verge of girls and baseball cards in the limbo of life. I was suspended in the water for a moment, and I was suspended in summer, between responsibility and childhood. And I knew it.

When I climbed up the bank, the kids were gathered around Ronnie, listening to his story.

"Then he pushed me. I fell down in front of all those people. So all I could do was rush him."

"You rushed Erik Krumel?" Pete asked.

"I never got to him. He clobbered me with a punch to the eye, then kicked me in the stomach. He gave me a few more until I hit the ground. He wears those big hikers. Someone said they are steel-toed, and I believe it." Ronnie pulled up his shirt and showed me a big puffy bruise on his ribs. Ronnie fixed me with a look with his one eye that held a tinge of blame.

"Krumel asked me where you were," Ronnie said.

"What did he say?" John asked.

"He asked where Jamie was. Told me to tell you he was looking for you. Then he kicked me in the ribs again."

Ronnie turned the other direction to show a black-and-blue bruise on the other side of his body. He probed the injury with his finger.

"My mom thinks two ribs are broke. It hurts when I breathe in."

A kid did a lot of breathing during the course of a day. We stood around him, feeling bad. None of us knew what to say.

"I thought he went to Lincoln Hills School and they threw away the key," Dave said.

"No, his dad is a big shot who owns a manufacturing plant. He gets him out of everything and puts him back on the street. They have a family lawyer who just gets Erik out of one mess after the other," Ronnie said.

"Your dad is a lawyer. How come you aren't rich?" Pete asked me. "I saw your dad in the park. He was talking to Dean's mom about how she might get his dad out of jail. Doesn't he have an office like anyone else?"

"No."

"Why does he sleep in the parks?" Rich asked.

I was embarrassed and ashamed, and then I was ashamed of myself for being ashamed.

"Who was Krumel with?" I asked.

"Diaz, Rennin, and Ron Thompson—the whole team of brutal assholes was with him.

"They bait him on," someone said.

"What did they do when you were getting beat... when you were fighting?" I asked.

"They stood around me and cheered, but didn't get involved," Ronnie said. "Had I put up more of a fight, I'm sure they would have joined in."

"Sorry, but no way are you putting up a fight against Erik Krumel. He's six-feet tall," Keith said.

"Yeah, and he has a square head. It would be like punching a block of wood," Pete exclaimed. Some of the other kids chuckled, but not too loud.

"Why is he looking for you?" Pete asked me.

"My brother, Tim, beat up his older brother."

"It goes back earlier than that," Ronnie said. "He has got an axe to grind with you."

"What did he do to go to Lincoln Hills?" Pete asked.

"He hit a kid on the head with a baseball bat and put him in the hospital," Keith answered. But I knew it was a few more incidents, one of which I had seen. The local movie theatre is the Cosmo in Merrill and it was good at getting the best pictures that were coming out. After a testosterone-charged movie, there was often a fist-fight behind it by the river bank.

When Chuck Norris came out with his movie *Breaker, Breaker*, the owner of the Cosmo took away a pair of nunchucks from a kid that was about to pummel another. The pre-fight hype was drawing a big crowd. But the little old man with a bald spot on his head, who ran the movie theatre, broke into the middle of the circle, grabbed the two, homemade, wooden sticks, held together with a chunk of rope, and said, "Every time you damn kids see a movie, you think you're all tough guys. Let me tell you kids something: Everybody is a tough guy. It takes a smart guy to stay out of trouble." He walked away with the nunchucks.

The rest of us dispersed out of lack of interest. But I had seen Krumel in action after the seven-fifteen movie, *Marathon Man*, had let out. Two guys, older than our age group, were waiting for Erik outside the theatre.

I happened to be behind him as he walked out the front doors onto Main Street. The older kids approached him fast and one threw a punch that landed on Erik. The solid hit should have floored him. But he absorbed it somewhere.

Erik responded with the speed of a cobra. He moved in and landed return punches to both of the attackers. His shoulders fired like turrets on an anti-aircraft weapon. He landed two hits to one man, pivoted, landed three to the other, and then swung back to the other to land a few more. He went back and forth like that a few times in impressive array. The older guys were not prepared for such a response.

Then, catlike, he backed off and took something off that was around his neck—a heavier-than-usual neck chain of some sort.

In his hands, it was a terrible weapon. The two guys moved toward him, surprised at his nine-punch counter-attack, and Krumel moved back with small half-steps, snapping the necklace like a gym towel at the faces and heads of the two attackers. The strikes landed hard and took immediate toll.

I still remember the sound, more than anything. The thinner chain's snapping, as is struck human flesh and bone, was distinctive, and rang of damage.

The metal moved like a lightning bolt in his fist and, when it landed, it laid open flesh. The second attacker lost the baseball cap from his head and threw both hands over his face. Blood poured out from between his fingers.

The first attacker moved in and swung at Krumel, who moved back and snapped the chain fast and hard. He landed three more strikes to his head. He mastered the distance between them with his footwork, taking half-steps back and using the advantage of distance to land devastating, snapping lacerations.

Krumel was smiling and laughing, like it was a big game they were all playing. He was enjoying this. To anyone passing, it might have looked at first glance like these clowns were screwing around. The three might look like friends that might just be having a little rough house. It would look like that for just a moment.

The coup de grace was when Erik wrapped the chain around the neck of the first attacker, used it to gain leverage, and rammed the attacker's head against the glass poster case.

It shattered and the attacker 'screamed like a girl' when he pulled his face out of the glass case, revealing a jagged cut across his forehead, over the right eyelid.

I watched it unfold, standing there in the doorway of the theatre. I had never seen, or have yet to see, someone handle multiple attackers that effectively with so little effort. In the aftermath he turned away from them, with no regard.

"Fucking pussies," he said to his two opponents, then spit a gob of blood on the nearest one. As Erik turned, he spotted me. He stopped. There was fifteen feet of night air between us, and nothing else. I was impressed. Okay, I was scared.

The short man who ran the place burst out the door and looked at the broken, glass poster case on the exterior of the building.

"Who the hell broke my marquis?" he yelled at Krumel's attackers.

The two older boys were pulling themselves up off the bloody sidewalk, staggering to their feet. I heard the broken glass grind under their work boots. They cradled wounds that had yet to be fully assessed and disfigurements they would carry as reminders of their underestimation of Erik Krumel. They lumbered down the dark street like zombies to the shouts of rage from the theatre manager, then vanished like dispelled spirits of the summer night.

Krumel had walked away, casually staying in the crosswalk. When he made it to the other side of the street, he looked back. He was laughing. I made my way home from the theatre with a creepy certainty that I was destined to clash with this larger-than-life opponent. It was fate, and nothing would change it from happening. I was onboard a big ship with a prearranged destination.

"Anyway, watch your back," Ronnie said, and slowly, painfully slipped off his T-shirt that read Get Bent on it. The cop would be circling back soon. I got on my bike—the steed that took me all over town.

I wanted to be alone and think this through. The uneasiness was a disturbance to the balance of peace that I sought. I felt a need to make council for war.

Ronnie was right about it going back further than that. Before my parents divorced, we lived on Lake Pesobic, just outside of town. It's a cute, little lake with a small community that knows each other. Our friends were reached by motor boat. We caught frogs and swam in the summer, hunted for rabbits in the woods across the road, and skated in the wintertime together on the shoveled-off lake ice. We were the lake kids.

Summertime on the lake brought new life, new friends and people to their cottages. And those people brought friends, kids, cousins and nephews to the cabin for vacations. The lake community could quadruple in population overnight after Memorial Day.

One of those boys was Erik Krumel. He was an okay kid to hang out with. We got along great for the most part. He was overbearing and arrogant. I pride myself on being able to hang with anyone and have fun. There really was no sinister drama that I could think of. It was a small occurrence, but it meant something more to him than it did to me.

We had been catching crayfish, placing them in a coffee can, and watching them fight. They didn't really fight, but clawed at each other for a moment. We argued which one had won and, in response to my claim, Erik had surprised me by tackling me.

We rolled around on the shore of the lake, punching each other, until old man Livingston came and broke us up. Erik had gone home to his grandma's house, a few houses down the shoreline. It was no big deal, and something that was not even unusual in childhood conflict.

A few days had gone by without him showing up, and that was okay by me. On the Saturday of the week, early in the morning, he appeared at the screen door of our house. I was eating a bowl of Boo Berry.

"Let's go catch frogs by the swamp end of the lake," he said.

"No," I answered around a mouthful of marshmallow ghosts.

"Then let's go fish for bullheads off the dock."

"No, I don't want to do that either."

"Do you want to go swimming?"

"No, I don't want to hang out with you today. I've had enough of you for a while."

"How come is that?"

"When we take on someone in a dirt-clod fight, if we start losing, you join their side and start throwing dirt clods at me. The other day you started a fight with me for no reason. I need an Erik break."

He fumed from behind the screen, then struck it hard with his fist, and it rattled hard against the door frame.

"But I don't have anyone to play with!" he yelled at me through the wire mesh.

"I don't care. Beat it!"

There was something dark in him that I didn't want to hang around anymore. Some people improve your life with their absence, and I felt he was one of them.

That moment was a part of this conflict, all of it. The tension was manifesting into a dark mass and gathering like a storm in the sky. And with my brother, Tim, winning an impromptu boxing match in the parking lot of McClellan's retail store with Erik's older brother, the entire dysfunctional family was most likely drawing a bead on us.

Tim had the rage. His confidence, sense of humor, and leadership skills gave him a gregarious edge in social situations. He was known in Merrill as "a tough kid who liked to fight." His sense of justice prevented him from being able to walk away from confrontation.

Shawn's big, Everlast, heavy bag in the basement had given him the edge, as it did all of us. To the sound of the rocking rafters and jingling chains with each strike, we three boys had developed the ability to hit really hard.

During an argument, while I was eating a bowl of cereal, Tim punched me in the stomach and I rolled on the floor in the Captain Crunch. Cold milk soaked my clothing as I tried to breathe with a collapsed diaphragm. All the while, the Flintstones medley played in the background with Fred banging on the door of his own house and yelling "Williaaamma!"

That was normal behavior in our house, and I saw it in others' homes where brothers grew up in close quarters.

The bike knew the way home from the bridge and I was transfixed in introspection. The threat of the situation was troubling me to the point of robbing me of peace from this summer, or so it seemed at the time.

I hated the threat of the looming confrontation with Krumel more than the prospect of the fight. He was deliberately victimizing people around me, using psychological warfare. That type of sick maneuvering was disturbing to me.

I needed to consult him to prepare for this epic struggle in my young life. I didn't want to wake up in a hospital bed with brain damage from a baseball bat, waiting to find out if I could ever walk down a flight of stairs again, like the Hanson kid.

I saw Tim's Corvair in the driveway and I found him in his room.

"I will have a problem with a larger opponent," I admitted. "It will be violent, and there is no way to avoid it."

"What the kid's last name?"

"Krumel."

"Is his brother's name Robert?"

"Yes."

"I think that's the guy who attacked me in the parking lot of McClellan's. It didn't end to well for him."

"Great."

"Is this trouble you have coming from that?"

"No, I don't think so."

He looked down at his book for a second.

"That guy is a major asshole and had it coming. I didn't start it, but I ended the conflict."

Tim threw a Nerf football at me and I caught it—a connection made.

"I could intercede here, inject myself into this conflict, but eventually you will have to face it on your own," Tim said. His eyes were fierce under his Peter Frampton hair.

"I understand."

"Come on, let's go down to the heavy bag and work on this.

In the dank basement, he assumed the role of instructor.

"You're shorter, so you have to stay in tight. Get inside his reach where you can bomb him with the heavy punches we've developed on this big leather bag. Bomb him with left and rights. If he backs up, stay with him and throw elbow strikes. Grab his head and pull him into head butts. Remember to strike with the crown of your head—keep your chin down. Throw knees to his groin and legs. If you aren't rolling your shoulders with heavy punches, you're throwing elbows, knees, and head butts. You can only win by fighting inside."

He blasted a few punches into the bag. It rocked, the chains rattled, and the floor boards creaked above.

"That's all you do. Got it?" he asked and demonstrated elbows, knees, and head-butts again.

"Sure. I got it."

It took a little practice, but the idea I got.

"If you step back, or allow him to pull back from your clutch, he will pick you apart with punches and kicks from a distance. Also, if he gets a hold of you and the fight goes to the ground, you will be in trouble."

"I wrestle."

"Look at me!"

He slapped me across the face.

"On the ground, only weight matters. How many times do you get on the mat with someone out of your weight category?

His fierce, Irish-green eyes blazed on me.

"In every one of these fights, remember you are fighting for your life. When you weigh less, you generally don't want to go to the ground. So we fight to win. Got it?"

"Yeah, I got it."

The slap pissed me off and I thought about closing fast for some elbows, knees, and head butts, but discarded it quickly, liking the way I was thinking, though.

"It's not a fight you are going to look for, but it sounds like it is looking for you," Tim said.

"It is."

"I understand. For every one of these assholes I have problems with, I didn't start it. You get in one fight and everyone wants to try you out. This is going to be a tough road, you know?" he said to me and let that sink in.

"You can prepare, start training and, if I am around, you know I will help."

Tim always had my back. A few summers earlier I was at the Formica breakfast table. Tim was sliding off his chair to go play football with the neighborhood kids on the lake at Dave Haxton's house.

"Why don't you take Jamie along with you?" Mom had said. She had made it an almost habit to throw an anchor line between us as he was leaving. I wanted to go but didn't want to be assigned.

"Yeah, I can play football," I attested. I liked hanging out with his older friends. I learned new lingo, heard dirty jokes, listened to what girls they thought were pretty, and heard playback of fistfights or wondrous deeds of magnanimity about the other kids on the lake.

"He can't tag along. This is a big game and we have sides picked already."

"He goes with you. He needs something to do today," Mom said and returned a gallon of milk to the green fridge. A radio played Freddie Fender—"Wasted Days and Wasted Nights."

A few moments later I was double-stepping beside him down Lake Pesobic Road that would take us around Johnson's Point and then to Haxton's. It was still early morning and the birds were singing a symphony as we passed. A mist from the lake blew under us and down the asphalt road, lifting my heels.

"I have to take you everywhere I go. You're the little twerp that hangs around my neck like a lead weight."

I kept pace and looked down the road.

"When me and my friends are around, you need to learn to take off. Nobody wants a little kid around. Got it?"

"Got it!"

When we arrived, the older boys, Tim's age, were throwing around the football.

"You brought Clunk with you," Bob Schmidtke remarked.

"Clunk, a hunk, a piece of junk!" they all called out in unison and then laughed. Clunk was my nickname. As a baby, I was called Thumper by my mother. Tim changed it to clunker. It meant dog poop, as in "You stepped in a dog clunker." So the nick name stuck to me and I still get called it today.

The game went on in the small yard of the Haxton house. I got in the way of most of the plays and was trampled once and knocked down twice during a play. The moment came when Dave had the football. He ran in my direction, thinking me as the weak link due to my size. I moved to intercept. He stuck out his arm to stiff-arm me off, but I ducked and hit him low.

I got a grip around both of his legs and took him down with a superior tackle that flattened him and sent the ball skidding out of his hands. Bob Schmidtke picked up the fumble and ran it in for a touchdown.

Dave got up, furious at being bested by the little kid on the field.

"Why don't you just leave, Clunk. You don't know how to play and no one wants you around here anyway," he said in temper.

I looked at the anger in his face and scanned the others. In the sudden silence they looked at me. I looked each one in the eye in a left-to-right scan. I saw indifference, sneering, impatience—stuff I had seen before. The moment hung there and I let it. It had taken us this long to get to the ending of this experience. I didn't see any advantage to rushing it.

Then I decided that I had had enough of these older kids. Older or not, they could be real jerks, and they didn't look so cool anymore. Leaving after flattening Dave was a good way to walk off his property. I started walking off the field. I heard a familiar voice from behind me break the silence and I stopped in mid-step.

"Hey," Tim said to Dave. "He goes, I go."

His thick curly hair stayed still in the gust of wind.

"Well that's just fine and dandy. You can go, too," Dave said with the football palmed in one hand.

The two of us walked home that Saturday morning together. We didn't say anything, and nothing needed to be said. We left the way we came there that day, as Finucans. And that day, I learned what that meant.

With Tim's instruction, I felt slightly more prepared for the apocalyptic showdown. The summer was too long to be able to avoid Erik Krumel for much longer. And, as I lived my little life, I was beginning to feel like a scared rabbit taking cover in a birch pile. The image of me and Robbie Grefe—jumping on brush piles and then shooting at the cotton tail rabbits as they darted out—flashed through my mind.

I left the training session with Tim and stood in the yard watching the late afternoon light filter through the trees. The majestic pine trees dropped an acrid, sweet smell of needles and three crows talked to each other from the green tops. I got on my bike and blasted off down the driveway. If I pedaled fast enough, I could outrun the floating, nauseous feeling in my stomach.

In my blue notebook I wrote:

Gross Joe stepped into Brenda Manix's apartment to be met by Lieutenant Simms.

Hey lookie here, it's Gross Joe. What do you want?" Simms said.

"Brenda asked to see me about something. When I got here, I find you 'so called cops' going through her stuff," Joe said, looking over Simms' shoulder at the other cops in the room.

"Well, she's dead, so you can beat it. We don't need no flat-foot Private Investigator hanging around," Simms said. "You know, if your nose hairs get any longer you can braid those things."

"Nice haircut, Joe. Did you get a free cup of soup with that?" another cop said, and they all laughed.

"You guys mind if I use the bathroom? I gotta go real bad," Joe said, looking stressed. Simms let him in and Joe went into the clean bathroom and unloaded his bowels like he could on command. He was just about done on the toilet when he heard the cops in the apartment start choking from the smell.

"Jeez, Joe. What kind of road kill you been feeding yourself?" Simms called through the door.

"I'd tell you to light a candle but the place will blow up. Crack a window before you leave. We're going out to smoke some sulfur and share a smelling salt to get the smell of what you did in there out of our noses," another cop said around a choking hack.

When Joe came out of the bathroom he found the apartment empty. This gave him a chance to rifle through her roll top desk. He found a picture of Brenda standing with Jenny Wilson. Joe looked close at the photograph. In Jenny's hand was a knife, and she looked like she was going to stab someone with it.

CHAPTER 8

Honor your father and your mother, so that you may live long in the land the LORD your God is giving you.
Exodus 20:12 NIV

I never know when I'm not writing. Sometimes my wife comes up to me at a party and says, "Dammit Thurber, stop writing."
James Thurber

Dad and I were huddled under a picnic table as the rain came down. A thunderbolt blasted loud and close, and the rain fell thick around us, as if to drown out the air. Dad had set up a little sleeping arrangement at the end of the park. When the deluge hit, we had only the picnic table for cover. Dad had thrown the horse blanket that was his bed, over the table and we dove under it.

The water came down, soaking the blanket, and dripped down between the boards of the table. The grass beneath us was wet but soft. I had brought a box of animal crackers and we ate them in silence, while the rain pounded down around us and dribbled in periodic streams from the spaces between the boards.

Dad broke down and sobbed with a giraffe cracker in his hand. He cried from his stomach, bent over in despair, and groaned in agony. I moved my legs; the water was getting my jeans wet.

"Maybe you should go home, little buddy. It's getting late and I can't offer you much hospitality," he said between breaths. "I'm broken right now." It was hard for him to be alone, but hard for him to be seen like this by me.

"No, I'm fine. I'm okay," I replied, not really wanting to leave him alone, but not knowing what else to do. I thought of having to run through the rainy park with the Indian ghost outside. Then running all the way down the dark trail that ran alongside the Wisconsin River. If I was tomahawked, no one would find me until morning.

"How did your studies end for last year?" Dad asked, gasping for breath, trying to steady his hand.

"Fine. I got an A in English." I lied without knowing why.

"That's good."

Dad slipped away somewhere in grief again. A flash lit up the makeshift tent for a split-second, then thunder crash-blasted just above us.

"Do you think the rain will stop soon?" I asked.

"I sure hope so."

Dad looked out from under the horse blanket into the rainy park.

"I'm going to get a wet ass sleeping out here."

"The river will be high tomorrow morning. Maybe we can float sticks and throw rocks at them," remembering a time when we did that and laughed. I wanted him to remember a happy image.

"We'll see."

Dad's eyes were wide and he floated away from me. I had lost him for the night now.

"You had better run along now. Your mother will wonder where you are. I had a hard day and I need to get some sleep. Come back tomorrow sometime and find me someplace."

"Are you going to be OK here?"

I remembered his super power—to be able to fall asleep fast.

"Sure, little buddy. I'll be fine. Now run along."

He lay down exhausted. A line of rain water dribbled down on his arm, unnoticed. I flipped back the horse blanket and scurried out, like a rabbit.

I ran home through the rain. The water fell down around me and looked like bouncing nickels on the pavement. This sound grew louder and my clothes clung to me. I imagined that I was running home on a big net, and had to land each foot on a network of roped connections, or fall into a river of lava beneath me.

I had seen a Tarzan movie where Tarzan had to knife fight this big tribal warrior on a net with boiling lava beneath them both. I ran home in an imaginary knife fight against a tribal warrior with the thunder and lightning crashing around me. The streets of my little town were not streets. I was a thousand miles away in a native jungle with snakes hanging down from the trees and black panthers springing out from the courthouse steps.

I made it home, soaking wet, exhilarated. I took off my wet clothes and went to bed, not giving the day another thought, and was lost in a child's dream for the night.

* * *

Swimming lessons at the pool were cold-weather, water survival training for kids. Mom's insistence on those classes is why, today, I can swim across the lake at the cottage in Tomahawk. We learned how to flutter kick, holding small Styrofoam boards out in front of us. This built in me a strong crawl stroke that I use to swim the rivers even today.

When we were ready, we jumped into the deep end—the pale, blue abyss, where we learned to stay on the surface and tread water in training for the big finale—learning to make your clothes a floatation device. The class was run by high school kids, guys and gals, that took it seriously, worked hard, and were focused. We learned to swim at a new level during those classes.

At the end of it, after hard work, they failed me, and made me take it again the next summer without moving ahead.

The class started at seven o'clock at the city pool. With the morning temperature about 50 degrees, a mist of precipitation often hung in the air like a cool extension of winter's finger. Fifteen of us kids from age eight to eleven would be in our swimming suits, crouched, holding ourselves in our own arms, shivering. The last thing any of us wanted to do was to jump into the cold water. This was before the concept of heated pools.

I can remember Mike Krewold, trembling and looking around at the madness of what we were doing.

"This is insane. Who would go in that water with the temperature what it is?" he asked me around blue lips.

We did. We stayed in the chlorinated, chilly water for fifty minutes, learning the back stroke, the crawl, and the side stroke.

"If I make it through this class today, I am going to find some hot water and lay in it for about an hour," Mike said. We had pulled the early June lesson; the kids who had the class in July had it made.

The pretty high school girl insisted that we jump into the water with clothes on and take them off, while keeping ourselves afloat, then fill them with air so we could hang onto the blown-up wet denim jeans, like life preserves.

"Jump in the water. Let's go," she hollered.

The hardest part was taking off the jeans, because it meant you had to sink. Your hands were full and your legs were caught in your pants. I remember struggling with my clothes and feeling gravity pull me down to the cement bottom of the pool, the air so far up above me.

I wrestled in the blue water, got my legs out of the jeans, then pushed off the bottom and propelled myself to the surface, clutching the denim fabric. I earned the right to breathe. At the surface, I tied shut the legs of the jeans. I blew air into the waistband and trapped oxygen in them. They buoyed up in front of me and I hung onto them.

"If the air starts to run out of your pants, splash water on them. They will hold air only as long as they're wet," the demanding lifeguard said. I treaded water on the floatation devise I had created from my clothing.

The action of the day started tumbling the lock on my imagination. The setting around me changed. The odor of imagination filled my nostrils with vanilla soup, then salty sea spray. I was hanging onto my homemade flotation device in the Pacific Ocean. Four-foot waves rocked me, lifting me up to their crest, then dropping me into a deep, aqua bowl of salt water until the sea surged again, lifting me up toward the high blue sky.

When I got to the cusp of the wave, three Japanese Zeros appeared on the horizon and strafed gunfire into the water in front of me in a triangulation. The bullets chopped into the water toward me as I rose and dropped down between the waves.

The thirty-caliber projectiles stitched into the water next to me. I lifted a bloody hand from the ocean water and held up a finger for the pilot to see.

"Go to hell, you Jap," I yelled.

"Hey, kid, what's your problem?" the life guard asked, pointing at me. She was sexy when she was mad, damn it. I pulled my arm back down into the water.

"Flip me off again and you are outta here. Got it?"

Her finger jabbed at me like a rifle barrel.

"Sure."

To me, she was an Asian on the bow of a boat with an automatic weapon screaming orders at me in a foreign language.

I remember coming out of the water at the end of that lesson, and feeling good about what I had learned. A sense of accomplishment welled up within me. There was bliss in growth and development.

With the onset of hypothermia, the class ended and we scampered across the concrete with our wet feet slapping beneath us. We rinsed off chlorine in the open-ceiling, cement locker room with a cold shower by pulling a big ancient chain. I had to pull with my weight on the metal handle and let the ice cold water dump down on me, stealing the air from my lungs and making my muscles contract. Then I turned in my chip to the kid behind the counter and he handed me my wire basket with my shoes, sweatshirt, and towel. The cement room echoed with the calls of boys in excited conversation, talking about baseball tryouts, famous athletes, or movies. The worst part of the day was over. The rest of the day was cheesecake.

But we would be back—my team and I. Tom, Chris, Mike, John and I would return at night, when the pool is closed and empty. Two big lights lit up the complex in beams lined with shadow. The water was mirror still and the moonlight shown on the theatre of the surface of the pool. The lights on the side of the pool still couldn't block out even the stars' reflections.

We arrived by bike in our swimming suits, then scaled the twelve-foot-high cyclone fence. It rattled under our assault. My feet pinched in the sideways wire squares. We dropped down to the concrete on our bare feet—swim suit ninjas.

For a moment, we all paused and looked over the empty pool. It was all just for us. There was a feeling of exclusivity, mixed with our intrusion that added to the excitement I craved. I climbed the ladder to the high dive. From up there, I could see the Prairie River wind past the high school and Third Street's traffic. I would like to see that pretty lifeguard try to stop me now. I thought of her as I ran out on the board. It was hard to see in the dark, and as I ran for the end of the diving board, my left foot missed the rubber-grip surface and I fell forward.

I hit the board with my groin, thigh, and then head. The corner of the plank was stiff and rough. A white bolt of pain flashed through my brain like the explosion of a star cluster. I tumbled through the night, spinning slightly, then splashed down into the water, just inches from the cement gutter.

I scraped my shoulder on the course wall of the pool, warning me how close I had come to slamming onto the pavement from twenty-five feet up. I thanked God as I ended the momentum of my splash down. Once again I had escaped death.

When I finally ended the momentum from my plunge, the force of the water held me. It called for me to stay here, in this weightlessness. The dark enclosure of weightlessness appealed to me on some primal level where it was quiet and so still. I moved slowly toward the surface. Shaking away the stars in my mind from the board, I clawed toward what I hoped was the surface somewhere up above.

'You ok?" Rob asked me, looking at my face.

"Yeah," I said and treaded water for a moment. The surface of the water and my position in it shifted for a moment sideways, and then leveled out again. All my components worked—a banged-up leg, sore head, and a scrape, but I was mobile. The sound of bodies plunging into the water orchestrated a symphony of action, whoops of joy, and yells of Bonsai and Geronimo that filled the night.

The plunges from the high dive into the night water were exhilarating. You could never tell at what point you would hit water. If you flipped forward and overshot the spin, you wouldn't know if you were going to hit your face until you did. A high dive could become a belly flop of pain with misjudgment in the dark air.

It had been a long night of play. We got to do about ten jumps off the high dive each before Pete gave a shrill whistle off his two fingers. I looked at Third Street and saw a police car driving by. The cop tapped his brakes as he passed, then turned the car around.

"Move out!" I yelled. We broke for the fence. The rush was there, but I felt good about our situation. It takes a little while to scale the wire fence. The metal pressed in hard between our toes when we climbed fast. We dropped like cats onto the ground as the cop car pulled into the parking lot. Once on our bikes, we headed for the bridge that went by the library. As long as we didn't get seen on the street, we would make it a few blocks away. We were good.

"So long, suckers," Pete yelled out when he knew we were clear. The night was warm and we were free.

In the notebook I wrote: Build a fort back in the pines. Things I will need: hammer, nails, wood slats from the fence and some matches to start a campfire. Get marshmallows!—and a can of vanilla frosting to eat with my fingers. (Underlined twice)

* * *

Dad was standing in the yard, puffed up, smoking a cigarette. His stance was wide and his shoulders were back. He wore his Browning Hi Power 9 mm in a U.S. Government-issue shoulder holster, slung over one arm.

"I just came from the sheriff's office. I walked right in there with Deirdre's ticket and threw it down on the sheriff's desk. I told him we are not going to have the second generation of Finucans get harassed and oppressed by the Lincoln County Sheriff's office."

"You did what?"

"Deirdre got a ticket for disorderly conduct. I threw it right down on his desk and told him, we ain't gonna pay it and they can stuff it. I had my weapon right over my arm, like this." Dad gestured toward the pistol.

"No kidding. What did he say?"

"He didn't say anything. He just stared at me. But damn it, I meant it. I am sick of the harassment by these pricks. Now this leaky attitude of the local law enforcement is spilling over on you kids, and it pisses me off." Dad flipped the butt of the Marlboro 100 away. I jumped on my bike.

"Where are you going?"

"I have a karate lesson that starts in ten minutes. I have to run."

I left Dad puffed up in a righteous rage of the family defender and rolled off on my bike.

The karate lesson was a brutal one. Being eleven in an adult class, I was disadvantaged. In here, people didn't care if you were a kid. This was karate sparring and it was time to unload. The adult students were understandably aggressive. And that was okay. And besides, eleven or not, I wanted to study just as bad as they did. There was something very satisfying about fighting with an adult.

What eleven-year-old kid wouldn't mind kicking an authority figure in the stomach with no recourse other than what they would throw back at you? And that was how it should be. Immediate lessons and immediate gratification was the advantage of a sparring class.

"A knife sharpens on stone. A man sharpens on man," the instructor said. I thought he was faking a Chinese accent.

My opponent, in the last session of the night, was a college kid and was a guest from another school, and another style. His stance was foreign to me, and he didn't attack, but waited for me to move into range and then kicked me with long legs as I tried to advance.

This was very frustrating for me, as he was a bigger opponent. The least I could expect was for him to bring the attack to me and thereby be vulnerable for a moment. But he would not attack. And I loathed him. He used his only advantage, being taller, to maximize the session with a smaller and younger opponent, and a child really. Did he need to stay safe from me? This caused me to attack more and be kicked hard repeatedly.

I found solace as I struggled against the larger opponent, that at least I was bringing the attack.

The change happened when I was able to skip inside and reach his gut with a sliding side kick, and when I did, I anticipated that he would retreat to gain the tactical advantage, so I advanced with him, double-stepped, slid in, and landed two kicks and a punch.

I stayed in, where he could not use his long-legged advantage. In the close quarters, he could score, too, and did, but at least his advantage was negated and we exchanged contact.

With larger opponents, I had to stay inside. I had to control the fight with my footwork, the way Krumel did outside the theater.

I walked my bike home after the brutal karate session. My hip hurt from a side-kick I had absorbed from a cocky, older kid with a red belt. As I limped along leaning on my bike, images of Krumel using a necklace for a weapon surfaced like dead rats in the vat of my mind. I realized that Krumel was tougher than any of those people in that karate class. He would have kicked the crap out of anyone there tonight.

CHAPTER 9

When you and opponents have taken sides and are facing off, and it is not clear who will prevail, right then and there you stick tight to the opponents, so you cannot be separated, and in that process find advantage, determine how to win, and seize the victory powerfully.

The Book of Five Rings, Miyamoto Musashi

We are all apprentices in a craft where no one ever becomes a master.

Ernest Hemmingway

Dad and I were camped in the back of Riverside Park eating a late dinner of a can of beans and some hot dogs cooked on sticks. I had burned the skin on mine, but the inside was tender and moist like a boiled one never was. The bun seemed to taste wholesome and fresh in the outdoors. The moist, soothing air that rolled off the river brushed past us as we ate. When we finished, Dad drank coffee and smoked cigarettes in the final moments of the day.

I was tired enough to be able to sleep on the ground and started settling in.

"Does your mother know where you are?"

"Sure. She knows I am with you."

The wool blanket that I hid in the woods had gotten wet in the rain. The wool would still work to keep me warm. It was scratchy and moist, and smelled like earth.

I thought of what my friend Erik Lange said once: "It's fun to stay at someone's house until it is time to go to bed; then you wish you were back at home."

I could almost hear the river sweep by slowly, like a continuous, majestic train.

Dad flipped the butt of his cigarette into our little fire of thumb-thick sticks.

"If I could start my law practice again, we could get some money. Things would be different. I wouldn't have to live outside and be treated like I had leprosy. People treat you like you have a disease when you're poor."

"What do you mean things would be different?"

The smoke from the fire moved over the starlight and I thought I saw the image of a ghost.

"We could have an office with a secretary. It would have a waiting room here." He drew an image in the dirt beside our fire. "You could have an office over here—a corner office with a big window that looked out on some water; I know you'd like that. And mine would be over here." He scratched more squares in the dirt but already they were more than that to me. I saw it in my mind.

I thought of a pretty secretary poking her head into my office and telling me someone was here to see me.

"Cool. But I am not a lawyer. What would I do?"

"Every lawyer needs a private investigator—that's you."

"That's what I was thinking. What does a private investigator do for a lawyer?"

"Oh, there are lots of things they do. They serve subpoenas, interview witnesses, conduct surveillance, and follow people that we want to know things about."

"What's a subpoena?" I asked, pulling my legs up underneath me. Sleep could wait.

"It's a paper that if someone gives it to you, it orders you to appear in court at a specific time and day. It makes you testify in court. People try to dodge a process server. It's kind of a fun, crazy game. You would like it."

"Cool. Would we make money?"

"Sure, we would make a great deal of money. We bill out our time at a high rate—250 bucks an hour, at least. Sometimes we get a percentage of a financial settlement as well." Dad sat up and lit another Marlboro 100. "We could take cases, work them together, and be an unstoppable team. I wouldn't have to get treated like a bum anymore. I could use my law degree and your mother would maybe come back to me."

"A private detective. How about that?" I liked it, and thought of Gross Joe. "Yeah, that would be great."

I stared up at the stars with the visions of my dad's law firm in my mind. The wet wool reflected my heat and the fire crackled.

"I'm going to go out to Richard Putnam's tomorrow to do some more legal work for him. So I may not be around," Dad said, settling into his bedroll with his blessed ability to fall asleep anywhere. His activity reminded me of a dog circling on a blanket.

I imagined myself approaching Jenny Wilson, wearing a suit with shiny expensive shoes. She would be weeping into a handkerchief.

"Excuse me, Jenny, I know this is a hard time for you, what with your boyfriend getting his ass kicked for being a jerk and all, but I would like to ask you some questions. Do you have a minute?" I would play it to her cool, like I was almost bored and it was a long day of working hard as a private detective.

"Jamie, do you have to be so formal? We have known each other forever," she would say and reach out and touch my hand and smile through grief—the kind that took everything you had.

"Anyone you can think of who didn't like your boyfriend, Jared; I mean besides anyone who ever met him?" I would ask with a glance at a pretty girl passing by, who was looking me over like a manikin wearing the sale of the week.

I was just about to get the vanilla soup smell and take off, but Dad's snoring from the other side of the campfire interrupted my mental movie.

His snoring sounded like someone messing around with a chain saw, pressing the trigger in the guard for a little bit, letting the oil fly off the chain, letting it stop for a few seconds, then revving it up again, not real hard, but just enough to cut a piece of poplar about four inches in diameter. I listened and looked up at the summer stars and let the rhythm of the snoring relax me. I felt the ground pull hard on my tired frame.

My imagination soared over the park like a night hawk on a cinematic helicopter angle. I flew it over the dark park and moved toward a fire at the opposite end of the park. An Indian medicine man, who wore a full head dress, danced around a tepee-style log fire. He moved his feet in an even, melodic dance and thrust a big spear into the ground every tenth hop. From a deerskin pouch he pulled a handful of powder and cast it on the fire. The flames jumped up in response. His Chippewa song lyrics were beyond my comprehension, but the tones implied sadness, revenge, and a torrent of vindication. The music was beautiful and proper, though it did drip with rage. The smoke from the fire dance billowed up over the mighty Wisconsin River and tumbled on the rolling waters until lifted up by the breeze of the night.

The haunted park seemed alive around me, watching, waiting for me to fall asleep.

I was having a blast—just me and my dad camping under the stars, dreaming.

* * *

The next day I stuck with Dad because I knew Richard was coming to get him to bring him out to his farm house. I wanted to see the crime scene from the shooting, so I made sure I was there.

"Where is the Wild Counselor?" Richard asked me with a smile. He enjoyed Dad's sense of humor and I had laughed with them both for sometimes hours. Our stomachs hurt when we exhausted a session of hilarity.

When we got to the farm house, I milled around while they worked, discussing legal strategy and Dad poured over legal papers. I walked into the living room where the shooting incident took place. The window panes in the glass doors had been replaced and the glass had been cleaned up, but there were .22 caliber bullet holes in the wall in a steady line. The shooter had tracked Dad with the fire as he had rolled to the floor. The rage lit within me and smoldered.

I sat down carefully on the couch, where Dad had sat. I let my imagination replay it. Did he see in the window a silhouette of a man with a rifle? Or was he surprised by the first shot coming through the window. Johnny Carson was doing his monologue when the first bullets came through—crack, crack, and glass shattering. I rolled, imagining the bullets slamming into the paneling and couch, just behind me.

The shooter wasn't trying to scare anyone; he was trying to kill Dad. A television was a luxury for Dad. He had finally been able to relax from the constant stress of being homeless.

"When I'm at Richard's, I get what we bums call 'regular refrigerator privileges'," Dad had said to me.

I ran my fingers over the bullet holes in the paneling and touched the ones that had punched into the oak chair-board and base boards.

When the magazine in the weapon was empty, the shooter stopped. Dad had crawled over to his backpack and fished out his Browning Hi Power and racked a round in the chamber. He remained low and waited to see if the attacker would come into the house after him.

"What did you do then?" I asked him. He was telling me the story, standing in Mom's kitchen, like it was no big deal. That day, after the incident, Dad was wearing a gray shirt that said Marines across it. His Irish was up and he was ready to brawl.

"Who do you think it was?" I asked.

"The list could be a mile long. I made many people angry as an attorney. One thing is certain—the law won't do a damn thing about it. This psychopath is on the loose and wants to kill me. As if I didn't have enough problems."

"Why? Why won't they do anything about it?"

"Because I'm poor."

He had pulled the Browning pistol out from his backpack on the table, racked a round in it, and flicked on the safety.

"Well, I got something for the asshole next time he tries that." He looked at me. "We don't know who this is or what is going on, so you should operate at DEFCON 1. We don't know that this is only contained to me. Carry a weapon," he said.

Now, in the living room, I could hear them both laughing in Richard's office. Dad liked to mix humor with anything he could to keep off the depression. I went outside into the summer afternoon light. The farm was alive with chickens and a rooster strutting about the driveway.

Outside the patio door window, I found the place where the shooter had stood when he fired at Dad. Boot prints had sunk into the soft lawn; some by perhaps the perpetrator or the sheriff's office. There was no way to tell now.

It looked like a big boot print to me—a work boot, like the kind made at the Weinbrenner shoe factory in Merrill. I looked at the star-shaped impressions that the treads made. This type of footwear would be on a hunter or anyone who spent time outside. I put my shoe next to the print; it was twice the size of my foot.

I wanted to see it like a movie. I waited for my mind to create an image of what might have unfolded, but it didn't. Only a robin chirped from a nearby pine tree.

What would Gross Joe do in this situation? He would relax, look around, and think.

I squatted in the grass and moved the green blades with a small twig. I moved a pigweed and looked beneath it. I used my nightcrawler-picking eyes.

After using the twig for twenty minutes, my eye caught the distinct color and shine of brass. Under the weed was an empty shell casing.

I considered picking it up with some kind of object, like they did in the movies, in case it had a print on it, then I grabbed it with my fingertips. The shell was a .22 rimfire, one the cops had missed in their collection of evidence.

Gross Joe squatted down next to me. When I looked up at him he was staring me in the center of my eyeball.

"Look at that, Jamie. The cops missed a shell casing. They had a certain number of bullet holes in the wall. How did they not find the casing?"

"They were lazy, or didn't think to count the bullet holes and look for a certain number of casings," I answered him out loud.

"That's one theory," Joe said. He looked at me, like he was waiting for me to say something. When I didn't, he vanished.

I rolled the brass casing in the palm of my hand. At first it looked like other shell casings I had seen. A .22 was a familiar round to me. My friends and I hunted rabbits in the woods and a .22 was an ideal weapon. I squatted down in a hunch and settled in to study it, like when I made a burn in a table with a magnifying glass. I noticed something else.

On the side of the shell was a scratch, just about two millimeters long, that was very distinctive. The extractor on my rifle didn't leave a mark on the side of the shell like this one did. I put the shell in my pocket and kept looking around.

I walked a half-circle out from around the window, like you do when you are tracking a wounded animal, looking for a blood trial.

The sky seemed to fill up with low clouds in a moment, changing the light degree and my mentality with it.

Thirty yards out from the house, in the young alfalfa field, the dirt was soft. I found the impressions in the field where the shooter had walked to the farm house. The footprints that pointed toward the house showed that as he approached, his stroll was casual, and from the direction of the road.

Perhaps he had been smiling, chewing on a piece of gum, or whistling a soft tune. I played it again; he stalked up, like a sneaky assailant. The rifle clutched in his hands, or was it a pistol? A chill rippled down my spine.

I looked at the angle of the creep toward the house and moved in the direction that his vehicle would have been in, and stepped on the young sprouts of alfalfa carefully, and looked at the dirt.

I found a print where the toe of the boot had crushed a sprout and thrown up the soft soil to show how he had been running away. I tried to match the stride as I followed the prints toward the road. The stride between them was long. It must have been a big man as his running stride was twice mine.

He ran away, not knowing if he had killed my dad or not. If he would have tried to enter the farm house after the initial assault, Dad would have been ready with his Browning Hi Power.

I kept my vision down and followed the steps in the field under the gray overcast sky. I glanced up to see flashes of lightning up in the clouds to the north. I followed his steps until reaching the ditch of the gravel road, where they disappeared. I looked back at the field and let my imagination show me the figure running at me with the rifle in his right hand.

The shooter ran at me, had a big smile on his face, because he liked this stuff. It gave him a big adrenalin dump. When he got to the edge of the field, he slowed down to a walk. He didn't want anyone to see him running. He wasn't scared of anyone anyway. When he got to the ditch, he leapt across it with surprising grace. He was athletic and strong. The image of a man jumping over the ditch passed before me. The distance was at least eight feet.

The wind picked up and a crow called from an Elm tree by Richard's house. I felt a psychic finger touch me with darkness. A tingling in my bladder and scalp brushed me–the same that I experienced just before I wiped out on my bike or slammed my hand in a car door. I turned to look down the road.

I saw a yellow pickup truck about eighty yards down the dirt road, and I froze still. I couldn't see Gus's scratch but it looked like Derik Lawton's pickup truck.

The driver was inside the truck. He held his hands in front of his face. It took me a second to realize he was watching me through binoculars. I stared at the truck knowing that the lenses of his binoculars were focused on my face. I could only stand there and stare back.

I blinked. This wasn't my imagination.

The big man lowered the binoculars and started the engine of the big, Ford pickup and threw it in gear. He spun the back end of it around, threw up dirt from the road in a fishtail, and sped off. Above the yellow truck, clouds that looked like enormous fingers extending out from a hand stretched across the sky. Thunder rolled and flashes of lighting appeared in the giant, black hand in the fingertips. The truck vanished under a cloud cover of a fist-full of lightning bolts.

*   *   *

Erik Lange and I were sitting at the picnic table in the back yard of my house making improvised explosives. I was listening to Shawn tell Dad that he had decided to join the Marines.

We were both silently cutting out two-inch fin-shaped pieces of cardboard from a Wheaties cereal box that had a picture of Bruce Jenner on it, and taping them to the sides of a shotgun shell.

When we threw them high into the air, the fins would catch the air and control the direction where it would land. We would tape a piece of Styrofoam over the primer end and poke a roofing nail through the Styrofoam so that it rested on the primer. When the shell was thrown, the fins would make sure it fell on the roofing nail, and the shell would go off. I moved the cardboard as a I cut, rather than the scissors, like I had been taught in my educational classes.

Dad and Shawn were talking, standing on the green grass of the backyard, surrounded by the big majestic pine trees that brushed a hiss in the wind.

"I think you should reconsider," Dad was saying to Shawn.

Cars buzzed by on the highway through town, occasionally honking at who might be at the Dairy Queen.

"I am joining the Marine Corps and leaving this fall," Shawn said. This wasn't that big of a surprise to me. He had been talking about it for a year, and hung a poster showing a grizzled Marine fighter coming out of the ocean with a rifle in his hands, walking next to a black inflatable raft. The poster read, 'The Few, the Proud, the Marines.'

"You don't want to do that, Shawn. I have no doubt that you are tough enough to handle it. But do you want to do things like stand in line for hours looking at the back of someone's head? Do you want to be given orders to do what you are told and made to comply or serve jail time from the result of a court martial? I know what it was like—I was a Marine. And, Shawn, I have to tell you, you don't strike me as a guy who wants to take orders from someone else. You are a leader."

"I have thought about it a long time and I appreciate your support," Shawn said and smiled.

Erik looked over at my side of the redwood picnic table and saw what I was doing.

"They can be cut a little bigger. See what it looks like in the book?" He pointed to the copy of *The Poor Man's James Bond* on the table.

"Ok," I responded and moved the cut-open, empty, cardboard box in a wider arc, right through the face of Bruce Jenner. When my last one was cut, I picked up the black electrician's tape and started taping the cardboard fins onto the sides of the 12-gauge shotgun shells.

"Look, think about this—give it another year," Dad said.

"I have been thinking about it, and if you won't sign the papers, I will as soon as I turn 18."

The two of them walked off toward the house, while we finished making our little bombs. They were a mess of black electrician's tape and cardboard fins with a nail sticking out on top of a Federal shotgun shell. I hefted the device.

"They're called Nut Busters," I said.

"Don't drop the damn thing," Erik said calmly. He was holding himself differently as we worked on the bombs, sort of posing like Douglas MacArthur, only missing the corn cob pipe. We put them in a shoe box and walked over to the parking lot of the DNR building, which was closed on Saturday. There were no cars in the big, glorious parking lot where we often threw around a Frisbee or a football.

Today, it was the testing ground for our new weapon.

I grabbed the first of the Nut Busters. "Fire in the hole!" I yelled and tossed the 12-gauge shell into the air, high over the parking lot. We both dropped down to the ground and lay flat. The fun was in those moments of anticipation, as the shell fell, to see if simple science was this reliable.

We should be safe—I played it out in my mind. The shell lands on the nail, the nail drives through the Styrofoam, strikes the primer of the shell, the shell explodes, and the birdshot goes straight up.

The shell soared into the air. When it landed, the explosion rocked the air and scared off the crows in the tops of the pine.

We got up off the ground and cheered. We spent the afternoon lobbing up shotgun shells, diving to the grass, and watching them explode on the pavement.

As I hefted the last one, I wondered if I shouldn't save it for when I had my confrontation with Krumel. But, try as I might, I couldn't see it working out in the theatre of the real.

CHAPTER 10

Each man is a hero and an oracle to somebody.
Ralph Waldo Emerson

You don't have to do much, you just have to show up and be the medium for that unconscious to deliver what it's prepared.
Norman Mailer, on writing

"Hey, wake up. Let's have a cup of coffee." Dad had stepped into my room early on that summer day. He looked around my room. He was wearing cut-off shorts with holes worn in them and a T-shirt with a yin-yang symbol on it.

"This room is a mess. Here let me show you how to clean this up," he said and began picking up dirty socks and throwing them into a clothes hamper in the corner of the room.

"No, you don't have to do that. I will get it later." I was irritated and not interested in entertaining people at 6 AM on a Saturday. He saw me look at the alarm clock on the night stand.

"Get out of bed. The sun is shining and it is a beautiful day." He was organizing things in my room, setting them in what he saw as their proper place. He hung a pair of binoculars on a hook by the window, tidied up a deck of cards, and jammed them into a book case. He picked up a book I was reading.

"Are you reading O. Henry's *Cabbages and Kings*?" he asked slightly surprised.

"I am. I like it." I swung my feet out of bed. "Meet the day head on," I said to myself.

"See, if you organize your room, it reflects on your mind. If someone walks in here and sees all this stuff lying around, they will think that your mind is disorganized and you're unfocused," he continued, dusting off a dresser top with a dirty sock.

"Really, does it work like that?" The prospect that seeing into someone's mind could be as easy as looking at their room intrigued me.

"Oh, yes, your outer world is always a reflection of your inner world. As within, so without. It cannot be any other way."

In a matter of minutes my room was tidy and straightened up. There was more space. I knew what was in the room at a glance and where everything was. I realized that I felt better about the situation and, in spite of being grumpy at first, I was glad to be visited by Dad.

"I still have some money from Richard. Let's go to Zettler's and get some breakfast and coffee."

Dad was in a cheerful mood and it was contagious. We sat in a booth in the window at Zettler's. We laughed so much that the other people in the diner glanced at us.

After the eggs and hash browns with Tabasco sauce, Dad lit up a cigarette. "You should not be sleeping late, Jamie. You should be up preparing for life. It's good you are reading. I'm proud of you. Read the Russians, like Dostoyevsky. Immerse yourself in classic literature and don't rely on these teachers to hand you an education.

"An education is something you have to extract from this world, not be handed. It doesn't get pounded into you from some nitwit teacher and it doesn't happen to you just by being alive. If you don't extract it with a passion and desire from this world, you will be like the rest of these dumb shits walking the earth."

A big Cadillac pulled up to the curb outside our window and a slick dude of five-foot-nine with greased-back hair got out wearing a business suit. A Jeep pulled up behind him and stopped behind his Cadillac. A woman got out of the Jeep and approached the handsome man.

"Keep reading all the time. Discipline your actions so that it shows in your lifestyle. Discipline is in the little things in life, Jamie; how you keep your room, how you schedule your time, how you groom your mind for action. It's a requirement that you be mentally tough. You don't know what life may have in store for you."

"What do you mean?"

"You don't know what could happen to you in life. You might have to live outside. God forbid that should happen, but if you become disabled like me, life can be very difficult and it will take all you have and faith in God just to survive."

The woman from the Jeep was gorgeous in a Spanish-type beauty. Her hair was raven black in thick, styled clumps of curves. Her hips were generous. She had long well-muscled legs in high heels that moved like music when she walked toward the man in the Cadillac.

"Who is this?" I asked and called Dad's attention to what was going on outside the window.

"Trouble. That's who that is. It's Tommy Bracken and his future ex-wife. She is divorcing him. She's been having an affair for at least three years. Half of Tommy's assets are not enough. She wants it all. Tommy wants my help in this divorce," Dad said it like he was tired. The two, good-looking people argued on the sidewalk. Through the glass we couldn't hear what was being said, but the woman was speaking to him as though she was gnawing on a piece of leather.

"He's hurt. He really loves her and she is just scalping him like a pro."

Her face was angry and she jabbed a finger at him as she spoke. Tommy listened as though he had heard it before. He looked up at a bird flying off the building top and I knew what he was thinking. He was wishing he could fly away from his life. Did anyone envy a bird as much as I did?

The woman's beauty was exotic to me. I could understand why Tommy Bracken had fallen for this vixen, though now it was clear, through the window, that he was regretting his affection. He had been in love and now all he wished was that he could fly away.

Later in life I came to the conclusion that if you marry the wrong girl, you end up talking to yourself. Both Tommy and his wife were talking at the same time, neither listening.

The sexy woman walked back to her Jeep and drove away. The man walked into Zettler's diner and found us both sitting at our table.

"Pat, good to see you. Do you have a second?" Tommy asked and sat at our table. Dad introduced me to him and Tommy poured himself a cup of coffee from the white plastic thermos. "We have a hearing coming up on Monday and I was wondering about something that I want to bring up."

Tommy wanted to bring up how his wife was drunk and had driven their kid around while wasted on Manhattans. She had driven over a bike rack at the park when she was picking up young Alan from a little league game. She was doing cocaine and was banging the carpenter who had done some work on their house. Did he have any recourse? Did it help to get this out in the hearing? Tommy wanted to know.

Dad listened. He was good at listening and asking the right questions.

But I knew he had heard it before, because I had heard a similar problem with another divorce while eating a cherry-filled, sugar donut right here at the bakery coffee shop. Today, I was eating a chocolate custard Eau Claire. The massive sugar load was giving me the temporary high and the table was confining to me.

Sometimes I had heard Dad give tactical legal advice about how to file a motion to suppress something or some other way around a problem, but today Dad was tired of it all, I could tell.

For a moment, he looked around the diner as though he had not known where he was. Then he spoke.

"Here is my advice, from a guy who has gone through it. Let it go and walk away. It didn't work out the way either of you wanted, and each of you feel sorry for that in your own way. Take it from me: sometimes in life, what's more important is that you get out of this with your humanity intact. What's more important than the way things begin, is the way they end. Give her everything and walk away, if you can. Myself, I just can't seem to walk away.

"I don't know what the hell happened in your marriage, but if you can give her everything and come to peace with it, do it. If it will make her think more of you and value the experience of having married you, then it's worth it to do just that. Give her everything," Dad advised.

"If you can get away from this with nothing, but still function, consider yourself very blessed."

I knew to let the silence settle over the table for a few minutes before I made a move. When I did, I took a dive into the thick, cherry jam, surrounded by still-warm, baked, gooey, fresh dough.

Dad had time for the broken. Being broken himself, he understood and was their helper, even if he just calmed their legal fears. He used his legal skills to even the score of what he felt was unjust. But he was broken as well, so I wondered how much help can a wounded man be?

I walked home and left them discussing the issues of the upcoming hearing. It took me three blocks of sunshine, breeze, and birdsong to shake off the rattling bones of Tommy Bracken's broken relationship. They seemed to drag behind me, like tin cans on a string tied to my left ankle, clattering with every other step.

* * *

I ate Mom's lasagna with heavy forkfuls and washed it down with the creamy, white milk. The clock over the sink indicated I had only fifteen minutes to get to karate. The lasagna had cottage cheese in it and sometimes green peppers. Mom's meals were healthy—full of vegetables and wholesome ingredients, and made with love. Later I would realize what a great cook she was, when I would eat endless, frozen pot pies and peanut butter and jelly sandwiches.

I got on my bike and raced through town with my gym bag over my arm. A blue, classic, late-sixties Chevy Nova drove by with the windows down. "She's Not There" by Santana was rolling out in a wake of smooth rhythm.

The karate lesson was in a building that was owned by the Odd Fellows Society and they charged the sensei a reasonable rent for a big, wide-open room. I changed into my gi in the little locker room and bowed to the dojo before stepping onto the cool, wooden floor. The class was big tonight; four rows of people were lined up, six in a row. When sensei came out we began our stretching routine.

I breathed deeply and lowered myself over my tense legs and felt the muscles tighten, at first in resistance, but then they stretched and gave, extending with a burn so that I could touch my toes. Breathing, I had learned, was so vital to any level of performance. We stood and began our drills. The stretch had invigorated me and settled my reactive mind.

We began with kicking drills; round-the-clock kicking it was called. Front kick, side kick, back kick, back kick off the other back leg, side kick, front kick, again and again.

I was learning hard lessons about footwork and closing distance on an opponent. Taller opponents meant "get inside" and stay "stick tight" to mitigate his advantage.

The dojo gave me a sense of belonging and acceptance that I needed. Though I hardly spoke to the people in the class, they felt like friends with a shared interest. We knew more about each other from sparring than we could have by exchanging pleasantries.

Tonight was demonstration night. The instructor pulled a towel off a two-inch brick braced between two others. He stood before the brick and put his hands on his hips. We sat on the hardwood floor.

"I would like to do this today to underline that you kids should always listen to your parents." He took a rigid stance of concentration, poised his right hand in a fist on his hip, loading his weapon. With a loud Kia that came from his belly, he slammed the edge of his hand down on the brick. The smacking sound was the voice of the brick refusing to give under the strike, reverberating on the bare walls.

It was the sound of reversed energy rather than dispersed. It was the sound of pain.

Sensei, stunned, looked out at us collectively as though we might explain what had just occurred. We only stared back at him in the silent room.

The larger-than-life figure before us was becoming life-like. Sensei went into his stance and yanked once on the ends of his black belt, wringing some ancient strength from cinching the cloth. He exploded into another loud Kia that sounded a little like a wounded animal. The smacking noise sounded again but not as loud this time.

I looked at some of the older students. No one seemed to know what to do.

He struck it again, but clearly the only thing that was going to be breaking in the demonstration was sensei's hand. The silence seemed endless. Sensei, standing with his long hair and beard, looked like a man trapped before headlights of an oncoming truck on Highway 51 on a foggy night.

And I knew that image. When riding as a passenger with my mother, a man appeared in the dark road and mom had to swerve to avoid striking him. She corrected just before we went into the ditch at fifty miles an hour.

The man in the headlights of Mom's Dodge Dart had looked at us with that same expression—surprise and surrender to the incredible circumstance, because there were no options.

A diversion was required. I looked around and considered an option. I could backward roll three times, grab a shoe and whip it at the window, then yell something like: "Everyone out, carbon monoxide leak!" Then tear out of the room.

I pictured myself running down the street full blast in my bare feet and karate gi. The image struck me as hilarious and I held my breath. On no, this was not the time to crack up laughing. Not now. The pressure mounted in my chest and throat, and somehow this added to the hilarity.

With everything I had, I was resisting letting out a suppressed laugh. My head must have looked like a raspberry. My laugh broke loose like a rattle against the back of my throat. It sprayed out of my neck like machine gun fire. In a tight grimace I fought against it with all my life force, but that only made it worse, and it fed upon itself. The image of my cousin Pete and Mike cracking up at inappropriate times flashed across my mind and I let out another, and another, before it exhausted itself.

I was steeped in shame.

"Sir, may I?" student John Simon asked. He was a tall man about twenty years old and was Sensei's prize student. With his fresh, new, black belt wrapped around his bright, white, creased gi, student John approached the brick like he had already broken it. Sensei couldn't speak. He only looked defeated and waved his hand toward the brick for John to break—the brick he had set up.

But John was already stepping toward the brick, not needing the invitation. He hesitated for just a second, then dropped down with his weight in the strike, and with the confidence required, he split the two-inch brick like a ginger snap. We applauded.

The class began leaving the dojo without the formal ending. Sensei stood stunned, a shell of a man now, watching us file out like he was lost and didn't know where to go.

In the locker room, John was proud of himself.

"That was a good job you did out there," I said when we were in our street clothes.

"Thanks."

"An option in that situation might have been to strike the brick and act like you couldn't break it. Then let the class disperse. When all the students were out of the dojo, say something like 'Hey Sensei,' then break the brick with only him in the room," I related as I pulled open a bunched-up sock.

John looked at me for a second.

"That's a cute story. But it wouldn't be honest. To hide the face of reality would only perpetrate further self-delusion, and no one should do that. It lacks integrity, one of our core principles in Tae Kwan Do."

He shouldered his gym bag, closed the locker door gently, and walked out like Caine from the 70's television series, *Kung Fu*.

* * *

I could find Dad sometimes at the T. B. Scott Free Library. He read books all the time, studying subjects like mountaineering and survival, William Shakespeare, or reading poetry by Blake or Frost. Among the things he usually carried was a book.

He read a book on investments and studied a particular company named Cooper Industries. He was convinced that this was a stock to buy if he just had some money.

To the dismay of the library people, he highlighted in the books he checked out and wrote in the margins in his unique, scrawling handwriting. He was perplexed, at first, that someone would care if the book had markings on it. "Did they ever think that they could be superb study notes?" he said, shaking his head after hearing the complaint.

If he wasn't in the library, I would check Stanges Park, where quaint bridges arch over the water inlets, connecting the islands like a Japanese rock garden of green.

Kids fished for brook trout with small poles. They lay on the bridge, focusing down into the murky water with unbroken concentration.

In that park, hours drifted by before you realized dinner time had passed. The sun raced across the sky and hunger raged in my stomach, but still it was hard to leave.

Dad might be leaning on the rail, looking at the water, and smoking. I might find him lying in the sun working on his tan, reading a spiritual classic by Thomas Merton, or delving deep into a book by Franz Kafka, and also having a paperback next to him on how to survive in harsh conditions.

Always among his few possessions was a compass. As his world came down around him, the compass was of some comfort to him—to be able to touch something that would say in which direction was North.

Dad could analyze something from different perspectives and discuss it by breaking it down to an outline, then relate the idea in clear terms that I could understand. This process amazed me. In front of Richard Putnam, he could lay out the prosecution, then the defense, and then punch holes in both sides. He discussed legal strategies in intricate detail that then revealed the key to solve the defense or prosecution.

Lawyers drove from Wausau or Rhinelander to find him in the park, walking toward us with a case file in hand to ask him if he had a moment. I would listen and feel so proud of him, though he lived in a park.

If he wasn't there, I would look for him at Riverside Park, a place of reprieve and silence in the haunted shadow of the T.B.

Scott Mansion, where we found shelter from the emotional storm of the summer.

I ran to Riverside Park to find him. My feet couldn't move fast enough to find my best buddy and my mentor.

Just after the bridge, I dodged left on the magic trail to Riverside. The trail is shaded, covered with pine and oak trees, with the Wisconsin River flowing close by that gives a smell of vastness to the air. The temperature on that trail is four degrees cooler, the haunted hill springs up on your right, and the smell of living leaves floods your senses. Even the dirt smells good.

I slowed to a walk and strolled past the ancient, concrete bandstand set into the hill where the City Band often played and Popcorn Dan, the one-armed caretaker of the T.B. Scott Mansion, sold his popcorn to the spectators, before he booked himself a ticket on the Titanic on his way home from a visit to England and was counted among the missing. Dad was sitting on top of a picnic table facing the swirling river. He was reading a book on his knee and leaning back on the table top.

"Hey, little buddy," he said and smiled at me.

"Hi, Dad." I climbed up onto the table top and sat next to him. "I notice you got a new backpack."

"Yeah, Richard Putnam paid me some money for legal services rendered, so I got this nifty backpack with these neat storage pockets all over it." He spun and put his hands on the stuffed, canvas bag with shoulder straps. "I can put my gear in this and carry it from one campsite to another." He opened the draw string on the top and took out a small Sterno stove. "The trick seems to be, to remember what pocket holds what item." His hands worked around the zippers.

"Would you like some coffee?" he asked as though I were seated at a kitchen table in a fine home.

"No thanks. How much money did he give you?"

"He paid me two hundred dollars."

"When do you think you will get some more money?" I asked, while swatting a mosquito almost the size of a dime.

"Who knows? I still have twenty-five dollars left of the money so I can buy some cigarettes and we can go to Chip's and get two big Blue Jay Burgers." He took a compass out of his pack and set it on the table. From the bag he took out a can of beans and opened the lid with a small, C-ration can opener he called a P-38. "I was in the Marine Corps and we ate C-rations and we opened the can with these," he explained.

"Is it hard to sleep outside all the time?"

"Yeah, it sucks being homeless. Life is hard sleeping on the ground; it's hard on your back. I'm getting old now and this is tough," he said while stirring the beans over the Sterno stove. "Reach in that bag and get a small spoon and the metal coffee cup. We are going to split this can of beans. Bushes beans are the best."

I reached into the bag and found the spoon. All of his stuff was always in order.

"Dad, why don't you get a job and a house?"

"I think about it and I just can't deal with it right now. I don't know what is wrong with me. I just fall apart. I get so I can't be around people. Sometimes if someone says 'hi' to me I shatter. I don't know if you can relate to what I just told you." He looked at me.

I shook my head, no; I couldn't. In fact, it sounded very strange to me.

"I look at everyone else. They are able to hold down a job and go to work, and at times I'm envious—What it would be like if I could do that. I think about it a lot."

My serving of beans was cold in the middle, but still good because I had not eaten yet that day and hunger was the best seasoning.

"But then I think, 'Here I am sitting in the park, reading. I have the day to myself and I don't have to go to work or put up with some boss's bullshit, or be subjected to some abusive psychopath who wants to make your life hell in the workplace,' and I think 'maybe I got it made.' But then I realize I have nowhere to go and I get treated like shit by everyone because I am poor."

"Dad, why didn't you rent a room with the two hundred dollars?"

"Because I needed a backpack. If I got the room, it would use up all my money and I still wouldn't have a backpack."

We ate cold beans sitting on the top of the picnic table with our feet resting on the bench, watching the river roll and swirl by like a parade. We were quiet while we ate. The sound of our spoons against the tin can mixed with the song of the blue jay in a far-off tree.

"I have moments where I realize where I am—a man who has lost everything—and I can't believe it happened to me," he said and set down the empty can.

"Like, if you were to get a job as a lawyer again, you could get a house, and live inside. Wouldn't that be great?" I didn't like the idea of my dad being homeless and needed to know if there was something that could be done.

"I never liked being a lawyer. Can you imagine hanging out in a court house, dealing with other lawyers? I hate the law business. I always have."

"Yeah, but you need a home."

He looked lost for a moment. His eyes moved around as though he didn't know where he was.

"Every time I think of re-entry into the work world, I get sick to my stomach. There's something unhealthy about working. What I need is a tent. It would be nice not to have to sleep outside."

"But you don't have anywhere to put the tent." I had to speak softly here. I knew that it was "all in the tone" when addressing the wounded.

"Well, then, I get to live anywhere, I guess. You see, in Zen, they say to live nowhere, is to live anywhere." Dad put away the Sterno stove and tidied up his backpack. Then he took the compass in his hands and opened the metal lid on it. There was a small, cut opening in the top of the metal with a wire through it. He lifted it to his eye and looked through the slit opening. "Isn't this a neat compass?" He folded down the thumb loop, cupped his hand around the device, and lifted it to his eye. "This is how you use it to take a bearing," he instructed and handed the lensatic compass to me.

The needle spun in the bezel inside the metal case until I tipped the magnet down on it. The arrow pointed at the river—north. It was light and solid, and held a G.I. Joe-look to it.

"Cool," I responded and handed it back to him. He put it into his backpack.

"What is your mother doing today?"

"She is going to work."

"Does she ask about me? Like, ask how I am doing?"

"No," I replied honestly. "Well, maybe yeah, a few times," I back-pedaled.

"She sure is a special woman. Did I ever tell you about the time I fell in love with her?"

"Yeah." I had heard it before. I wasn't in the mood for that mushy shit.

"I'm going to sleep back here tonight. If I stay far enough back here, the police won't find me."

"Did you see the ghost again?"

"No, just that one time. But it is spooky back here at night. I sleep with my firearm next to me. When you're homeless, you have to remember that sick bastards will cut your throat for your shoes. Happens all the time. The homeless are beat up, robbed, and killed, and no one cares." Dad took out some coconut, suntan oil and spread it on his arms.

"The last time I pulled out the Browning was when the black bear came into my camp out at New Wood Park. It was looking at me like I was something to eat. That was a creepy feeling. I didn't have to shoot it because it ended up wandering back out into the woods.

"So what is going on with you? What's it like to be Jamie Finucan?"

"Me and Pete jumped the fence to the pool last night and went swimming. It was a blast."

"Really? What was that like?"

"There is no one there, of course, because it's night, so we climb the wire fence. Like that would keep us out, and we jump off the high dive in the dark. The cops went by and we had to scram. It was perfect."

"That sounds like fun. I want to do that sometime. Will you take me with you to do that?"

"You got it," I assured him. "Also, there is a cute girl I am trying to talk to."

"Fantastic! What is her name?"

"Jenny Wilson."

"Does she know how you feel about her?"

"No."

"Ask her out to the movies. Go get a malt at Rexall with her after the movie," he said with a smile. "Women like it when you ask them questions and take a real interest in them. When they talk, give them your full attention. Compliment them and hold doors open for them. That makes them feel special when they are around you. Be a gentleman, always. Do you do that?"

"Sure, what is this—a lecture on chicks?" I asked and smiled.

"Women are so great. Take an interest in them. Whenever I did, I always felt my blood pressure go down. Women are one of the best things God ever created. I've known some really neat chicks in my life. I met some that would have made my life a paradise. Are you listening to me kid?

"Kids! You can't teach them anything," he said and tousled my hair.

I was thinking about Jenny Wilson as I walked home across the bridge that spanned over the mighty Wisconsin River. As the cars went by, I hung onto the railing and watched the white water spill over the rocks, making root beer-like foam that spun and eddied around in the current.

At the end of the bridge, a kid that I had seen around town rode up to me on his bike and stopped in my path.

"You Finucan?" he asked me.

"Yeah."

"Erik Krumel is looking for you. He's at the sand pits right now. Says you have the ass-kicking of the century coming." He looked me over. "I thought you would be bigger. You're just a little fucker."

"Gutless people like to fight people smaller than them," I replied. The kid stared at me, then snickered. He rode off on his bike the way he came. I knew he had been sent to give me that message. He had come looking for me.

I doubted Krumel was in the sand pits. I looked around but didn't see him watching me. I threw a front and then a side kick at an imaginary opponent in front of me. I tried to think of Jenny again, but I couldn't get lost in it anymore.

CHAPTER 11

"We Finucans don't fight fair; we fight to win. And we fight like a team. If someone picks a fight with one of us, we all jump on that person and kick the shit out of him."
Pat Finucan

Most of the basic material a writer works with is acquired before the age of fifteen.
Willa Cather

Tim and I were locked in deadly combat in the living room of the house. This happened often. He was four years older than me, taller and stronger. He was also a skilled boxer and certainly a worthy opponent.

But I had the Finucan rage going. It flared up within me like a match-head and fed me with initiative in physical struggle. Triggered by injustice that I felt, it burned cleaner than hatred and if it wasn't courage, it sometimes was all I had. Against Tim, who had matching rage, all it did was get my ass kicked.

His longer arms got a punch through to my stomach and the blow doubled me over and interrupted the action of my diaphragm. I couldn't breathe. I hit the floor with my locked-up lungs. He was walking away from me but I didn't need oxygen for a counter attack.

I jumped up, enraged, and tackled him around the ankles just right. He toppled like a tree and struck his head on the corner of the oak coffee table that used to be in Grandpa Jim Finucan's eye-doctor office on Main Street.

The sound was distinctive. Tim's head knocking off the oak table sounded like a handle of a throwing knife striking a pine board target. He lay on the floor, and didn't move. He started twitching, his arms and legs jolted in a series of spasms. "Hey, you ok?" I asked. But he was convulsing on the floor and flopping around like a bluegill on a dock.

I approached him carefully; I had to be sure this was not a trick.

"Tim?" But he just kept jerking around on the floor. I considered my options: wait for him to get up and kick my ass, or scram. I chose the latter. I escaped to a bright summer day outside. Sometimes the best place to be was anywhere but around that crazy house.

I knew when he woke up he would be mad as hell and looking for me.

"Like everyone else, get in line," I said out loud and ran out of the house for Blue Boats, one of the refuges of the summer.

The swimming hole was named by kids before us. And it was a place of reprieve and sanctity.

I don't know why it was called Blue Boats. I envisioned an old boat with faded blue paint on it, moored by a worn rope left behind long ago.

The grass was thick there and a stone, fire ring was used for parties at night. The trail led people to the site abruptly, and you never knew who might be walking right up on you when they rounded the pine corner.

Blue Boats was a great place to swim on a hot summer day, and it was just a short walk behind the house I grew up in. There was a bench there for a while. You didn't sit on the bench. You stood on it to push off, while you clutched the rope swing—

riding the pendulum momentum that carried you out over the water to the crest of the range of dangle before you let go.

I had perfected a dive off the rope swing. I pushed off from the bench and swung out hard, then raised my feet over head and let go of the rope with my head pointing toward the water. I plunged into the dirty water of the Prairie River, just getting my hands extended before my head made contact with the surface.

I arrived at Blue Boats by myself to find the bench missing. I looked around the riverside campsite but there was no sign of it. I made the jump for the wooden handle that dangled from the tree branch, which was the only way to get it. You had to commit to catching it and jump out over the water, and in the vital instant, wrap your hands around the thin rope or the wooden stick handle.

I ran toward the water with rope in hand and drifted out in an arc over the water. I raised my feet over my head and intended to dive off the rope swing like I had so many times.

At the last minute, I changed my mind. Something was wrong. I could feel it. My subconscious was telling me that it didn't like the missing bench. I dropped my feet back down, abandoning the impulse to dive, and let go of the rope. I hit the water and instead of plunging into it, I bounced on the surface, off the bench that someone had placed in the water, strategically where someone would land on it coming off the rope. They had stood it up on its end so it would have the ability to do massive damage to the jumper.

I slammed into the bench and pain filled my back. I crawled out of the water, thankful to be alive and able to move. Had I done my dive, I would have been dead. I pulled the bench out of the water slowly. There was no way I could leave that like it was. The pain I was feeling from the back injury that day would haunt me all my life.

Had I decided at that moment to dive I would have certainly perished in the river from a neck or head injury.

I wondered how nefarious this attempt was. Was it a random act of shit heads screwing around, or was this the work of someone who predicted I would go there and tried to kill me? On the way back home, I played out the image of drowning while crippled in the water. My corpse would not be found for days, and when it was, it would be bloated and white like an upturned old fish.

I limped down the trail and the thought of Erik Krumel putting that bench there crossed my mind. The accompaniment to my back pain was the unnerving feeling of being hunted, again.

* * *

The phone rang at my mom's house and I answered it on the third ring.

"Is Jamie Finucan there?" the adult voice asked.

"This is," I said. My mind flashed through a million reasons why an adult was calling my house and asking for me by name, and none of them were favorable.

"Jamie, this is Warren Kleinschmidt with the *Daily Journal.* You applied for a carrier route job last week. Is that right?"

"I sure did."

"Well, your house is located in a good area and we need a carrier to distribute the papers on Wednesday, Thursday, and Friday of every week. Can we count on you to do that job?"

"You sure can."

He went over the particulars about what I would be getting paid and what the duties and responsibilities were, but my attention was jumping all over the place. I had a job. I was an important member of society. Those roads everyone was driving on? My tax dollars would be paying for them; I was a tax payer now. I imagined myself chewing out teachers and cops, "Hey pal, you know who pays your salary? Me! Now get out of my face so that I can go to work to finance this crooked town."

I would have money now, real money from a job—money for dates with Jennifer Wilson at Dairy Queen and then a movie. I would have money for burgers, the fair, sporting equipment, or just money to buy things on impulse, like graphic novels at the drug store, or *Creepy*, or a *National Lampoon* magazine. I imagined eating at the A&W restaurant across the street, reaching for the check with my friends at the table. "I got this," I would say, and throw down a wad of cash that would stun them.

"Can you get me a paper route, too?" Dave Weber might ask.

"I'll pull some strings and see if I can't make that happen, Dave, but it's a big responsibility."

"I can do it. Just get me the gig. I promise I won't make you look bad," Dave would probably say.

I stepped outside in the sunshine of the summer afternoon, the long shadows in the early afternoon hinted at the summer vacation passing away. Dad was in the yard with a cigarette clenched in his teeth. He was smearing coconut oil on shoulders so dark they could only be on a bum.

"Hi, Jamie. What are you doing?"

"Dad, I just got a job, a real job," I responded, bubbling like an upturned garden hose.

"Oh, yeah? What job is that?"

"I got a paper route. The papers get delivered on Wednesday, Thursday, and Friday. I deliver them, and then I collect the money at the end of the month."

"You have to collect, too?"

"Sure."

"Well, that really sucks. You mean they are running a business and want to shove off onto you all the responsibilities for delivery and collection? How much are we talking here? How much are you getting from this deal?"

"About ten dollars a week." If I had been wearing a vest I would have hung my thumbs on the front of it. "That's real jack.

I could start saving for a car, take a girl to the movies, or have a pizza at the Pizza Hut when I wanted to."

"That's not enough. This job is going to suck. This is the summer. You will be playing with your friends and then you will have to leave and say, 'Oh, this really sucks, guys, but I have to go deliver papers.' Then you're going to have to lug those papers around and deliver them to people. And let's face it, some of these people are assholes and when it comes time to collect, they are going to pretend they're not home, let the dog out of the house at you, all kinds of schemes, and for what? Ten bucks a week? That is not worth it," he said and flipped the cigarette in the driveway of Mom and Bob's house.

"You should tell these people to shove that job up their ass."

The butt sparked when it hit the gravel, then tumbled until it laid still, the white smoke trailing up.

Dad turned himself to face the sun and sat back in a strapped lawn chair.

"Listen, kid, I am going to tell you something. There are only two good days on a job, and that's the day before you start the job, before you realize what a bunch of shit you got yourself into, and the day after you quit, when you realize how lucky you are that you don't have to do that bullshit anymore."

"Really? Two good days?" My smile was feeling tight and aggravated.

"That's right," he said.

The DNR station next door left the radio on loud in their trucks and it squawked from their parking lot. The DNR rangers were working. They had to be there today. They would have had to call someone and tell them they were sick if they didn't want to be there.

"You are young. Your summers are yours. This is the best time of the year. Don't screw it up with a job. Screw the system. Screw the man. Stay free."

I looked at him. Dad was free. He was broke, homeless, and destitute. But, he was, in some ways, free.

I thought of the swimming hole, playing football or baseball with my friends, riding bikes, and fishing in the river. I thought of how I looked forward to summer through the tough school year. Every summer was magic and I wanted to embrace it.

"Yeah, you are right. What do I do about the papers that are going to be delivered?"

"Call them back and tell them you don't want the job." He said it like it was the easiest thing in the world.

"But I kind of gave my word."

"No, you didn't. You changed your mind. You are a free citizen of the United States and you can take a job and change your mind if you want. You are making a different decision based upon new information," Dad said, sitting in his clean, worn-out shorts and sweatshirt with holes in it. His expression of justification was on his face and his eyes searched mine from under the thick gray hair that was a mop on his head—uncombed today.

I went in and made the call. When I came outside, Dad was gone. I jumped onto my bike and blasted off into the cool breeze of a Northern Wisconsin summer day, one of the few in life, to find some fun. I had my whole life to work. This summer was for living.

*   *   *

In my notebook I wrote:

Borrow the book *Jaws* from Don Brose. Big shark that eats people. (Stick figure of a guy swimming with a fish biting his leg.)

Gross Joe was pissed. He got out his favorite glass, the Green Bay Packer one that his dad had given him when he was a kid, and dropped three dirty ice cubes into it.

They clinked in the bottom like stones in a wishing well.

"I got every psychopathic asshole in three counties trying to kill me and the cops around here with their head up their asses, deliberately." He walked into the living room of his trailer, turned on the television, and sat down on his couch.

All of a sudden, bullets came through the window, spraying glass all over him.

Joe was pissed and drew his 9mm Browning Hi Power and unloaded it back through the glass. The fine weapon rocked in his fist and fire blasted out from the muzzle.

"Bet you weren't ready for that, you fucking grease ball!" Joe yelled and ducked for a moment.

Joe moved around the house with his weapon reloaded and a flashlight in the other hand. He found the dickhead who shot at him. The guy was lying there dead with about nine bullet holes in him, six of which were in his ugly head.

Gross Joe kicked him to make sure he was dead. Then he spit on him with one of his huge, nasty luggies that stink like crap, and walked back inside to finish watching *Mannix*, and freshen up his drink in his favorite glass.

"All these assholes are going to have to get in line," he said to himself.

* * *

The summer was deliciously warm and I flew my bike down the streets to Karate class. I made a corner on Mill Street and saw the blue AMC Hornet that Krumel rode around in. He was in the front passenger seat, saying something to the driver. His squared-off head and thick neck gave the appearance of a bull in the car.

He didn't see me. I proceeded on my way. I slammed my bike down outside the karate dojo that was above the bakery and headed up the stairs to the Society of Oddfellows Hall.

My state of mind was dark. The darkness threw a shadow on everything I saw and robbed me of my usual level of joy.

The smells of dusty, wooden floors, old paint, and time permeated the changing room. As I put on my gi, I heard sniffling from the kid on the other bench. He was a few years older than me and I had never got to know him. I didn't dislike him; he was a loner. They had their code of silence.

As he put on his gi, he broke down and cried, blew his nose in a piece of crumpled-up newspaper from his pocket, and wiped his face with the big, droopy sleeve of his white uniform. I gave him the decency of pretending that I didn't notice, because that's what I would have wanted. I left the changing room.

A few eight-year-old kids were running around the dojo before the class. The instructor was talking to a student about a testing date. There was an air of normalcy here—a routine that was comforting. This was a place I was accepted and the rules here were something I understood.

The class started on time. It lent to the sense of order. The kid that was crying in the changing room entered the class and took a position in the line next to me. I moved down to let him in and the chain of students moved down in response.

It's a way the class recognizes that someone has joined the group. I see you. You are acknowledged.

We stretched for ten minutes. The tension moved out of my legs. I leaned forward, pulling the muscles open, stretching the tendons out. The muscles in my back tensed, then released. I breathed out, and collapsed against my legs, stretching out, feeling longer, more complete. I breathed deeply. It lowered my heart rate.

I was uncoiling, displacing stored energy, releasing acids into my blood stream.

I exhaled all the air from my lungs and lay my forehead to my knees. I was entering into the state of mind that would increase my reaction time and sharpen my focus. I relaxed.

The room was quiet and we were prepared for our workout.

The kicking exercises were stern: round-the-clock kicking, jump kicking, strikes and blocks. Then, time for sparring. I turned to spar with the kid with the issue that had been crying in the locker room. He bowed with a minimum motion to me, indicating his level of respect to me, the dojo and ultimately himself.

"Fighting Stance" the instructor said. We pivoted, and I chose Knife Hand Guarding Block. He chose the Low Guard, a stance that I had been unable to get past last time we sparred. This afternoon his eyes had fierceness in them that I recognized. The residue of pain, crystallized into determination, looked back at me. It spoke to me as I crouched down in my stance. I would answer.

"Fight," the instructor called out. It echoed off the hardwood floors and the naked wood paneling. We flew into each other in a clash of arms and legs that left me with a fat lip and three bruised ribs the next day. He expressed his dissatisfaction in life with kicks, and I blocked. My opponent unleashed a fury that came from his anguish, so I responded in kind and committed to the honor and privilege of unleashing my own, and found a sufficient supply of rage to touch.

He pressed in upon me, bigger in stature and with more weight. At first I was forced to retreat, then I remembered to collapse the distance and take away his advantage. I moved in tight and stayed there. It worked.

When the round was over, I looked to see for the first time that the other students and the instructor had stopped. They were watching us clash.

"Turn to your opponent," the instructor called. Everyone snapped in. The kid turned to me and looked me in the eye this time. The fury was diminished. So was mine.

"Bow," the instructor directed. We bowed. This time he bowed low.

As I got on my bike, the heat of the afternoon enveloped me like a sauna and I made my way home slowly, my energy spent. I could not guess what that kid's problem was but I knew this, I had helped him deal with it. Sometimes all we need is a challenge to remember who we are and where we have come from.

And as I passed Chip's Hamburgers and smelled the fresh, ground beef sizzling on the grill, I felt the darkness had vanished from my mind. Activity had changed the biochemistry of my brain. I remembered a quote: "I must lose myself in activity or I will wither in despair."

*   *   *

Some of Dad's friends were the forlorn and dejected; people who were broken in spirit drew toward Dad. Men who were going through a divorce, facing jail time for buying cough syrup, or sometimes on the verge of being homeless themselves.

Some were brilliant, and eccentric, and struggled with human relationships at the personal level. In many ways they were like Dad. They were funny, gifted, and tortured.

A young couple needed legal papers filed to stop from being evicted from their home after the guy lost his job at Kolbe and Kolbe. A forty-year-old man, who looked like he was sixty, came to find Dad because he was facing jail time for his third drunk-driving charge and just couldn't do the time. He sat down and listened to them first. He was silent, made eye contact, interrupted only when necessary for point clarification. He ran the risk of getting into trouble for practicing law without a license.

Paul Olson was one of them. He showed up at the strangest times. There was never a rhythm to his appearances. I recall on one occasion how he wandered into Dad's camp after he had just been let out of jail following a fist fight with his brother at his father's house.

A blue Rambler rolled down into the parking lot, looking like a match car from my Hot Wheels collection. He rolled in and knew right where to find Dad.

He tipped his head up and shook his long, dusty, ponytail hair over his shoulders and spoke with his face turned upright, at a slight right angle. He twitched when he spoke. I thought he could sing "Feelin' Alright" like Joe Cocker—like a pro.

Tagging along with them, I got to see Dad in action one day at a Pizza Hut. His mind was brilliant, as I had heard. I learned to follow his analysis of cause and behavior, and predict what the other side would do next.

"These are the three options that the prosecution has," Dad said and picked up an ever-present legal tablet from his backpack. He flipped past a page with writing on it, "All the exhibits," which had a list of some type of evidence. His pen flew over the page as he talked. He left behind block-style print that expressed only the point of his idea.

Ponytail guy was Paul. As his eyes closed, his head tilted back. He had a mystical appearance like a wizard or Tommy Chong. I waited for him to start an incantation.

"I refuse to read anybody's shirt, man," Paul said. "Messages that people wear posted across their chest are flagrantly disruptive and demean their own identity. Can you imagine making yourself a bill board, even paying to do it? It's ludicrous. And people say I'm crazy."

After a sausage and pepperoni pizza with the crushed hot peppers and mozzarella cheese, Paul sat back and said, "Now someone could eat this and convince themselves that they had a good meal."

"I thought it was pretty good," I piped up.

"Now that's what I'm talking about. But there were no vegetables. The grains you ate had the nutrition baked out of them and sopped in grease. You would have been better off going hungry."

Paul told Dad a story about how he was fighting with his brother about things they had inherited—a house, some money, a tractor. The lights were dim and a clock on the wall announced that it was always time for pizza.

"No, this is where you are wrong, Paul," Dad countered. "Your brother is mad at you because you punched him and stole his car. He is not without reason to be angry with you. Your conduct was substandard. You demonstrated a violent lack of self-control. Your brother is holding you accountable for your actions."

"The car was mine."

"No, the car was left to your brother. You would like to believe the car is yours, but it's not." Dad let that sink in with silence for a few moments. "Your actions are impulsive, emotional, and giving the impression that you're not in control of your faculties. I tell you that because that will be your family's point of legal attack, when it comes to the estate. Do you understand me? Old friend, I understand. I, too, am out of control. I have become an outcast, like you. But you can't go around punching people. No one here, Paul, has to take your abuse."

I shook out some of the crushed red pepper in my hand and imagined the waiter, suddenly turned assassin, and I had to throw the fistful of crushed red pepper in his eyes, upend the table and roll over it to kick the crap out of him as he tried to counter-attack with a balisong butterfly knife.

I had pulled the "It's always pizza time" clock off the wall and was using it as a shield against a skilled attack when Paul finally spoke.

"He was really being a jerk, man."

"Violence is a very serious and dicey thing to deploy, Paul. It's a huge force that you put into action, and it can quickly get out of your control and become something else. Your brother could have fallen down after you punched him, hit his head, and died. What would you have done then?"

'I would have had a party, man!" Paul called out.

I thought of Tim hitting his head on the coffee table and froze. There was going to be a fight about that.

Music was playing—a song by Styx, "Come Sail Away." Paul took up the chorus and began singing along with the song—loud. "Come sail away."

He sang the chorus once, stood up, and began singing it again with food flying out of his mouth. He raised one arm, then the other like a Roman senator addressing a coliseum. As he screwed around, I got the impression that he had performed somewhere before a crowd. He demonstrated an element of confidence and mastery that I found to be inspirational. He was fearless.

A family glanced over from their meat lover's bonanza with mild interest at the bearded, flannel hippie, pantomiming around and singing tone-deaf and off key.

"Is that Tommy Chong?" a lady asked her friend at the table behind us.

I sat there watching the spectacle with embarrassment and yet the scene appealed to my eleven-year-old revolutionary mentality. My friends wouldn't believe this spectacle. Dad was a step below being fed up with this odd ball, who was starting to get on his nerves.

I recognized this symptom. It came with fatigue. It pervaded an attack of depression that would plunge him into the depths of human despair that few can even imagine. He needed to be interrupted with positive regard for something. A story of nobility and/or light humor, but I could think of none.

When Paul was done, he sat down and sipped his coffee like nothing happened. Even the people around us resumed their conversations.

"That is an interesting way of avoiding a touchy subject, Paul," Dad commented.

I looked out the window of the restaurant and saw the sunlight. Suddenly I didn't want to be around old guys. I wanted to escape the old and wallow in my youth. I said good bye and ditched out the door of the Pizza Hut.

A girl my age was walking toward me in the parking lot. She had a dark texture to her skin, black hair and a sweet demeanor. It took a moment for me to realize it was Trish Lawton.

She gave me a half smile.

'Hi, Jamie," she said. Her voice sounded like music at a carnival.

"Hi, Trish. How is your stay?" Her lavender smell touched me with comfort. We made small talk with lots of eye contact. I felt a sweet reciprocation when a tender smile of genuine joy touched her eyes each time I said something funny.

We walked together for blocks without a destination. She started telling me about a dress she was making. She turned and took my hand with both of hers and was saying something about "not a teal color" but "more of a baby blue," but my heart was slamming blood through my ears so loud I couldn't hear her.

A green, 1975 Plymouth Valiant went by with Fleet Wood Mac's song "Dreams" playing out the window.

* * *

I was walking past Deirdre's room and saw her packing a suitcase. She was sorting out some clothes and then folding them and putting them into the hard-sided case propped open on her canopy bed.

"Where are you going?" I asked.

"Oh, hi. Mom is sending me to Florida to live with the Gulotte's for a few weeks. She thinks it will be good for me to get out of here." Deirdre was moving slowly, with contemplation. I let a few minutes pass in silence.

"Is that a good thing?" I picked up a music box and opened it. Clair de Lune came out of it.

"I don't know. At first I was mad. But now I think it could be a good thing. I guess it's up to me. I am getting into trouble here. I had an accident with the car and hit a motorcycle rider in the Council Grounds State Park," she said with dread.

"What? How bad is it? Is he hurt?"

"He broke his wrist and a few ribs. Dad said the insurance company will pay him off with a big check and he will be okay, but I could have killed him. It's time for a change. I can't argue that."

"The Gulotte's are a hoot. You'll have a blast."

"Florida is very hot in the summer time," she responded and held up a skirt with a blouse to see if it matched.

"When do you leave?"

"Saturday."

She looked at me, then looked around her room at the big canopy bed, her stuffed animals and books. When she turned, she wiped a tear from her eye.

"Listen, don't worry about this. Everything will be here when you get back," I assured her.

"I know. That's the problem."

CHAPTER 12

Read no history: nothing but biography, for that is life without theory.
Benjamin Disraeli

In my notebook:

Remember: Invent a paint to go on telephone poles that looks like tree bark.

Also – get my third-baseman's glove from John Purcell's house.

Dad went to daily mass in his program now. He quit drinking alcohol and didn't touch it again until near the end of his life. But now he was sober, and a big part of his sobriety included daily mass as an important ritual.

He took his Catholic faith seriously and talked about it with me. His love for God is what let him keep the amount of sanity that remained with him. He would invite me to mass and I, too, found solace in the ancient rite.

During the sermon, Dad would hand me a small card from his missal that would have a prayer on it and a religious picture of Jesus Christ. I read the prayer and handed it back to him. Dad reveled in the satisfaction of doing something that was right. He was acting like a good father.

Dad was sometimes frustrated with the priest. He believed some of them didn't do enough for the poor. Dad's skills as a lawyer and an eloquent speaker put him in a position to believe that he was a prophet who represented the underclass of the world.

A statement of "how shitty the poor are treated in America" was never far from his lips.

Dad took that charge seriously, and he often spoke out in mass. When they asked for prayers, Dad said: "For the employers of this community, that they end their greed and provide a living wage for the workers." People stared at us for the rest of the mass. The "Employers," after all, were big supporters of the church.

"If that usher who stands in the back all the time gives me another sideways look, I'm going to stick a knife in his gut," Dad said as we descended the steps from St. Francis Church. "And that singer can't hold a note. Where do they find these people? We got Klem Kadiddlehopper with the banjo. What is he doing playing church music?" he said in disgust. "With a banjo?"

"It just seems like that kind of talk shouldn't be on someone's lips as they leave church," I answered.

"Why not? You don't think God might expect a better song service at the mass from these people? If they had any reverence, these people would have a better choir. You can tell what kind of parish you have by looking at what they do for anyone else. These people don't do anything for the poor. None of these people care about the poor or social injustice. The poor are just people to leak on."

"Let's go to Mom's house and make peanut butter and bacon sandwiches for breakfast," I suggested to break the train of thought. It had to be done early.

We walked the short distance in the morning sunlight and were met by the Springer Spaniel Gus, The Brave. His head-down, tail-wagging, welcoming demeanor set us both at ease. Dad and I ate the sandwiches in the sunlight. Gus, The Brave, studied us without making a move.

"Who do you think shot at you through the window, Dad?"

I threw a crust to Gus and he caught it.

"I've been thinking about that. It might have been someone that was looking for me, or it could have been Richard they were looking for."

"How do you mean?"

"I don't think anyone knew I was out there."

*　　*　　*

My friend, John Purcell, threw down three dead rabbits that we had dispatched with my .22 pistol. The small, wooded area around the Blue Boats swimming area was perfect for 'backyard hunting.' I had set a few snares before we left.

We skinned out the animals and I cut the meat from the bones. I fried the chunks of meat in butter while John chopped up some carrots, celery, and a red pepper he had found in Mom's fridge. We threw it in a crock pot to cook for the day.

I tapped his shoulder and said: "Follow me." Sometimes an adventure started that way.

I took off running, and he followed. We crouched low as we ran through backyards. We ducked under a clothesline.

When we came near the Lawton's house, I could see the yellow pickup truck and we crouched behind a line of hedges.

"You know who's house that is?" I asked.

"Yeah, Derrick Lawton lives there. That's his yellow pickup truck," John said quietly.

There was the same yellow pickup that had been parked on the road when I was looking at the tire tracks at Richard's—the same yellow pickup truck that Gus had prophetically marked with his claw at the Dairy Queen.

"I think that's who shot at my dad."

"Why would he want to kill your dad? What makes you think it's him?"

"I don't know."

Inside the house, three heads where visible. One was a brunette girl. Two others were men. The men got up and moved around. From our distance, about sixty yards, I could see the window was open on the hot summer afternoon. Getting closer to the structure was going to be a challenge.

"I am going up closer. I want to hear what they are saying," I whispered.

"The neighbors will see us if we get closer to the house," John countered.

I didn't see anyone watching. I moved. I ran low across the weed-infested lawn until I was next to the house. John followed me.

When we got against the wall, we were exposed to neighbors possibly glancing out the window. We were both breathing hard.

From inside the room, I heard Trish's voice—confident and sweet, with a Cajun accent that caused an emotional crush inside me. She said something I couldn't make out. Her dad's response was loud, angry, drunken.

"You are damn right you won't," Derrick said. We heard the screen door slam and Trish walked right past us without looking in our direction.

Her subtle strut of confidence and personal pain created a furious beauty. Her books were clutched in front of her, over her heart like a shield. I fell in love with her right there. My heart went right out to her, and part of it would never return.

I don't remember how long we stayed there. There seemed to be nothing to learn, so we moved cautiously back to the fence line where we had more cover.

Just as we were about to leave, a car pulled into the driveway and parked behind the yellow pickup truck. The car was one I had seen before. A woman stepped out and walked up the driveway. I knew her. She was a girl friend of Richard Putnam's. The connection to me was important.

"Who is that?" John asked.

"It's a woman I've seen at Richard Putnam's office."

"What's she doing here?"

"I don't know."

We found out. When she came up to the door, Derrick Lawton let her in and put his arms around her. They went to her butt and he squeezed a handful. When inside, he pushed her gently up against the wall and put his hands on her. And she liked it. They kissed in the window.

"They got a thing going on." I sang it like the Me and Mrs. Jones song.

"They sure do," John said and then started cracking up. He was laughing louder than I was comfortable with and, when the two lovers got inside the building, I peeked over the fence. When I did, I was staring Lawton and the woman right in the eyes. I froze.

"They made us," I said. John froze, too. We all moved at the same time. Derrick moved toward the door, and John and I broke cover and ran out of the yard. I glanced over my shoulder when I heard the screen door fly open and slam against the side of the house.

I saw Derrick running off the stairs toward us with a .22 rifle in his hands. We poured it on, cutting through lawns, jumping fences, surprising dogs in backyards, and rolling under hedges. I looked for clotheslines that could decapitate a yard runner. I kept waiting for the crack of a rifle and a bullet to hit me at any second.

John zigged, I zagged, and we raced until we cleared a slat-wood fence. I glanced back just before jumping over the fence and saw the tall man with the rifle tucked against his shoulder, taking aim. When I hit the ground, I sprinted, feeling my heart beat in my chest. My legs seemed to weigh sixty pounds each.

We ran until we passed the bowling alley and got behind the big building, then doubled over, breathing hard.

"I thought we were goners," John said.

"Did you hear any shots?" I asked between breaths.

"I don't think he shot."

"That woman I've seen at Richard's office must have a thing going on with Derrick," I remarked.

"They got a thing going on." John sang like Billy Paul.

"So why would Lawton shoot at your dad?"

"He thought he was shooting at Richard. He was trying to kill Richard to get him out of the way of this perceived love triangle."

"If I knew a song that had the words 'love triangle' in it, I would sing it now," John replied.

"I need to keep looking at this," I mused out loud.

We stood there breathing hard, feeling lucky to be alive for the moment. The Finucan family had been in rifle sights twice in the last two weeks.

* * *

I was heading downtown alone when Chris found me.

"Come on," he said slapping my shoulder. "Follow me."

A Saturday in summer time held a sense of urgency about having fun. The summer days were numbered. Yet there were endless opportunities for fun ahead: fences for jumping, park benches for sitting, runs through a park, catching a stray Frisbee, or hearing a radio on, playing Jackson Browne's "Running on Empty" from a car nearby with its doors open.

We crossed the park and picked up Dave.

"Where you guys going?" he called to us, struggling to keep up with our pace.

"Come on, we're crossing the bridge!" I yelled out.

The big bridge spanned the river from the downtown area over to the arms of the T.B. Scott Mansion. If it was the trees or the river grass, there was an aura that accepted you when you stepped off the concrete, under the watchful eye of the mansion, standing like a gargoyle on the hill. The mighty Wisconsin River roared a hundred feet far below over the rocks, making a whitewater tongue that extended below the structure.

Crossing the bridge is tense for little kids on the narrow sidewalk. The timid walk their bikes. On one side, the steel railing guides the trekker over the long gradual arch, while inches away, cars speed by at forty miles an hour. There is a bitter sweetness in feeling the danger on the edge of both threats.

But there was a better way to cross the bridge, for an eleven-year-old. Extending the length of the bridge was a pipe that ran all the way across. One foot in diameter, the pipe was covered in the dust of weather and debris from the bridge. It was just wide enough to stand on and walk on. For forty-foot stretches there was nothing to hang on to. I knew the three of them well, and had teetered, extending my arms over a hundred-and-forty-foot fall, sometimes waving them frantically, to gain balance.

In those moments, I felt the wings of death.

I felt like a tight rope walker in a circus. I breathed in the wind off the river and felt it in my hair.

The trick to surviving, if you did lose your balance, was to drop down to the pipe and clutch it with both arms. The pipe was big enough so that my arms couldn't encircle it, so staying on top of the pipe was crucial. The chicken-out maneuver was to bend your legs toward the pipe if you felt yourself in an inescapable teeter.

On more than one occasion I had hit the chicken switch and dropped, slamming down against the pipe, and then clutching it hard, my face bouncing off the metal, tasting blood in my mouth and smelling the grease from the pipe.

But not today. Today I was upright. I had fended off the dog, endured a deadly smoke bomb attack, handled a canoe trip to Brokaw when the Captain dismissed himself from command and duty, and radioed us extraction forces that got us back to Merrill, with the canoe. This was my day, as long as it would last.

One foot in front of the other on the pipe, no slipping. Even weight distribution, please. Oh, please.

I heard James Bond music playing in my head.

"This is a dumb idea," Dave said, when we had arrived at the beginning of the pipe crossing.

"Since when does that stop us from doing anything?" I replied and stepped a little further toward the end game, so far away.

"Why don't we just cross the bridge on the walkway up top?" he asked.

"Because they will see us," Chris said.

"Who?" Dave asked.

"They," I answered.

"Who are they?" Dave asked with the voice of reason.

"Only they know who they are," I responded and climbed up the concrete bridge embankment.

"And they don't like us much," Chris said. He spun around once, as he began, something he would never do over the water.

"Yeah, nor we them, for that madder," I said in my best Scottish brogue. I began the trek that took almost forty minutes of slow, methodical, concentrated pipe walking. The wind had pushed up a light mist from the river over the pipe. It moved a little under my shoes and gave the pipe a greasy feeling.

"Dave, you cross on top, take the sidewalk, and make sure there are none to thwart our escape. We will meet you on the other side," I called out behind me.

At first, it was easy because the ground was close. If you fell, it was survivable, but within another ten feet of traverse, the ground dropped away to a road and a railroad track beneath the bridge. By the time I was over the railroad track I was at least three-houses high. I could hear the cars passing on top of the bridge above me and the water rushing over the dam to my right.

There was no easy way out at this point; just forward or back, no other option.

My hands stretched out, though there was nothing to hold onto. Behind me, Chris was taking slow steps, trying to find a way to move without losing balance each time he lifted his foot. He was walking sideways when I glanced back.

"Got to find your groove!" I called.

"Hey, slow down," Dave said from behind Chris. I crouched down slowly and turned to get a better look at what was going on behind me. Dave was coming along, but slowly. He was unsure of himself and this whole deal. His posture was balled up and unsteady. He looked like an accident about to happen.

"Go back, Dave. Give us air support on this one. The pipe is greasy today," I called out and turned my attention back to the pipe.

Below my feet, the white water tumbled over the rocks. The rolling whitewater below gave me a sense of vertigo. I focused on a rivet in the steel structure ahead of me, so far out of reach.

The big steel girders looked comforting, if they could be reached.

My life was balanced on a rounded pipe. The drama and the adventure lured my imagination.

"They're shooting at us!" I yelled out to my friends behind me. They didn't get it. I imagined that I heard the sound of a bullet ricochet off the metal structure next to my head. The Bond music went into the second chorus.

My balance wavered and I extended my hands to gain balance. For a moment, I wondered if I should do the last chance grasp—drop onto the pipe with my stomach and try to wrap my arms around it before falling the hundred feet into the rocky water.

It took a moment, but I retrieved my self-command. The key was to focus on your breathing and look straight ahead. Try to think nothing. And don't look down. Relax.

I was halfway across the river, when I felt the vibration in the pipe and heard Dave yell in terror. What the hell were we thinking?

I crouched, turned slowly, and saw Chris looking back at Dave, who was clutching the pipe in the chicken-switch position of having bellied down to the pipe, rather than topple off it. He was clutching the pipe with both arms. The pipe was too big for him to lock them around the circumference of the pipe and his body weight was shifting, sliding around the slippery, metal surface.

He was not exceptionally athletic, and his scrawny arms and soft midsection began to slide off the top of the pipe.

He was trying to clamp his arms around it tight to stop the slow rotation that would put him under the pipe but his arms were not strong or long enough. The expression on his face was one of forlorn horror. But there was a resignation of fate in them, as well, that added to the horror. He had the eyes of the "disbelief of the condemned."

"Hang on, Dave," I called out and crouched lower to gain a better sense of balance. From judging the distance, I would not be able to move quick enough to interrupt his fall. And even when I got to him, what the hell would I do then?

The Saturday had turned from a screw-off mission to a critical situation—in a moment.

I moved fast, almost losing my balance. Dave's feet dangled freely and his arms clutched the pipe above him. His feet were kicking the air, trying to find footing. Cries of inhumane horror rolled out of his mouth, mixing with the sound of the rushing water below.

His hands were separating on the pipe. His fingers clawed on the metal rounded surface, out toward the wide edge of the pipe.

Chris dropped down on the pipe, straddling it. He locked his legs around it and grabbed the left wrist of Dave as it slid off the pipe. Dave was yelling, dangling by his arm. Chris was cool—the kind of cool that you never could guess that someone can have until there's trouble.

Chris's face struck the top of the pipe when the weight of Dave snapped in his grip. Chris slowly started shifting in balance, and began sliding around the pipe. Chris clutched his legs around the steel pipe harder but the counter weight of Dave thrashing below was pulling him around it.

I tried to hurry, but every time I rushed I felt only a fraction of movement under my shoes on the slick pipe. I walked the pipe fighting a tremendous sense of panic.

Chris glanced up at me, not saying a word, but his eyes bespoke catastrophe. When I reached the two of them, I wasn't sure what to do to help, so I grabbed Chris's shirt at mid-back and tried to pull him back up toward the top of the pipe. But that wasn't doing any good. I almost fell off the other side of the pipe. Chris was in my way so that I couldn't help or take the other hand of Dave that was waving in the air below us.

I had to get to the other side. That meant I had to jump over Chris on the pipe. The idea seemed insane, but there was no other solution. Hesitation here meant death for both of my friends. I hopped into the air and jumped over Chris.

In mid-air, I seemed to hang weightless, like gravity forgot me. I felt like a big, meatball moon on a fall night—the big, white moon that makes the night seem like an extension of the day, so you could just keep playing. In that moment I wondered what the hell I was doing.

When my shoes touched the pipe, they slipped apart and I fell on my groin, smashing my crotch on the pipe. I clung to the pipe and groaned. Crushing pain swept up through me, threatening my consciousness.

The horrible screams of Dave continued as I recovered. When I could move, I turned, clinging to the pipe as I did, to face the situation. On this side I could be effective. I reached down and grabbed the other wrist of Dave as it flailed in the air. Chris slid sideways to the pipe and clutched at me. I anchored, and the two of us stabilized.

We lifted Dave up and draped him over the pipe. The three of us clung there, like baby bats. We were all breathing hard and didn't speak for a full five minutes. I remember focusing on keeping my weight over the center of the pipe, and waited until my heart rate slowed down.

"I want to go home. I can't climb down from here," Dave said in a half-whisper.

"We have to walk off this pipe, Dave," I replied. "There's no choice."

"No, call the cops or something. I'm not moving." Terror framed his eyes when he looked at me.

"Forget it. That's not happening," Chris said. He knew what we all did—when the authorities showed up, it was a big deal, and whatever fun we had gotten from the experience was not worth the attention.

"What if some fireman or cop falls trying to help you. You want that on your conscious?" I cried.

"Get someone who can get me down!" he yelled in my face.

It took a half hour, but Dave came to grips with the fact that he was going to have to walk on the pipe and cat-walk his way the rest of the length across the river. I went first, trying to act like I was not scared shitless. The other boys followed without a word. We all seemed to know that if we lost our self-control, even just a moment, it might never return, and the kid who gave into fear would still be there on Sunday, twitching like a nut case, unable to move in one direction or the other.

After a near eternity, I jumped from the pipe to the bridge embankment, then to the solid ground at the base of the hill, beneath the shadow of T.B. Scott Mansion. I took a moment to glance up at it. The windows looked like eyes peering down on us. We had escaped the curse—this time.

CHAPTER 13

I could not doubt that this was the black spot; and taking it up, I found written on the other side, in a very good, clear hand, this short message: "You have 'til ten tonight!"

Treasure Island, Robert Louis Stevenson

"I feel like the joy has been wrung from my life, like water from a pair of jeans."

Dad

From my blue notebook:

Remember Gross Joe has a stick fighting scene on a pipe, over water, under a bridge! The dramatic conclusion! (Conclusion underlined twice with a drawing of two stick figures fighting on a pipe with sticks in their hands over water.)

Early in the morning I set out on my bike to find my buddy—my dad. I had with me two peanut butter sandwiches and a thermos of coffee in a paper sack. I wasn't sure if he had eaten lately and I knew how much he liked coffee.

I looked for a solo figure that might be standing next to a picnic table going through the gear from his backpack. I drove by the bridge. Sometimes he stood and looked over the rail, staring at the water while mentally crawling around in the dark, defeated corridors of his mind. I glanced down the streets that might show him hiking with a stick toward the church, on his way to an early mass. He often had his bible missal in hand; his backpack stashed somewhere.

I found him on the street. He was walking with the load of belongings in his backpack. His posture told me from a block away that the pack was heavy today; he was dejected.

He was looking down at the ground and walking slowly, oblivious to what might be around him. I rode up beside him.

"Hi, Dad."

"Hi, Jamie," he said from far away.

"I brought some food. Let's find a place to sit down and eat."

"I am not really hungry."

Cars were passing by on their way to work. The lilacs were in bloom and beside us three bushes blazed out their color like splashed purple paint on a fence. The smell was intoxicating, rich and sweet.

"Come on. There is a bench over here," I said with some enthusiasm. I heard myself talk like that when he was down and distant. He followed me to a bench in front of an eye doctor place and I opened the bag. "I got us each a peanut butter sandwich and made you a thermos of coffee." I took out the contents of the bag as though they were prizes at a raffle.

'Oh, I could get into that," Dad said and reached for the coffee first. A car beeped and someone shouted something at us.

"I have been talking to this girl, Jenny Wilson. I think she kind of likes me," I lied without knowing why.

"Well, that's nice, little buddy," he said, but his mind was unsettled and far off. The silence settled on us as we ate the thick peanut butter on bread.

"She is so cute. I think I am going to ask her to the movies. There is a Chuck Norris movie out called *Breaker, Breaker.*"

"I've been such a failure," he replied quietly. "I've lost everything. I screwed up everything."

"Hey, maybe today we could float sticks down the river and throw rocks at them. Whoever sinks the other's stick is the winner. We had a blast doing that a few days ago."

"I don't think so. Not today."

"John Purcell and I got into a fight with two goons outside of Fred's Bait shop. I had to punch this big fat kid in the nuts when he grabbed me by the head and tried to wrestle me to the ground. It's bad if a bigger kid takes you to the ground. Once they get their body weight on you, you just end up getting the crap kicked out of you while everyone cheers."

I bit into the peanut butter sandwich on Roman Meal bread. I had carried the damn things this far. I was going to eat one.

"I look at all these people going by. They have jobs, they have families, and they have a future. I have nothing," Dad said. The morning had a promise in it. An opportunity for anything was in the cool air. I could feel it, but Dad could not.

"Here, you should eat something, Dad. You will be hungry later." With distant eyes he bit into the peanut butter sandwich and sipped at his coffee. The coffee was black and thick. I liked to make it that way.

"What are you going to do today?" I asked.

"I will go to mass here in a little bit. Do you want to walk over there with me?"

"Sure. You are not a failure, Dad. We have a great time hanging out. Lots of kids would love to hang out with their dad."

"Thanks, Jamie," he said drifting away again. After we ate, I walked my bike beside him as we made our way across town toward the church. The traffic had dropped off. Everyone on their way to work had gotten there. They were where they should be. We had the town to ourselves again.

I kept trying to make conversation with Dad to take his mind off his troubles. Sometimes it worked and sometimes it didn't. At church, the mass was a reprieve. Dad sought solace from God. The tones of the mass, the prayerful procedure were comforting to us. Here there was hope because God didn't require everyone here to be successful.

This was Mercy Street. Here God didn't care what you wore or if you were rich. Here, it didn't matter what mere people thought of you.

"I don't credit most people with the power to think. Why should I care what they think?" Dad had said to me. During the mass, he handed me a prayer card with the picture of an angel flying through the night with a sword of fire. On the back was a prayer for the lost souls in purgatory. Purgatory was a place in the Catholic religion where people are trapped if they were not quite good enough to get into heaven.

The church called for prayers for these people, so that they would be allowed into the kingdom of God. I read the prayer and thought of Dad being in a type of "purgatory of brokenness," walking this world as a puzzle piece that just didn't seem to fit.

I handed the card back to him and he nodded to me. He had done a fatherly duty. He had expressed the most genuine kind of love for me, steering me in the way of eternal salvation. To Dad, that was more important than being able to give me money or resources.

That was all he had, and all he could do at the moment.

* * *

Gross Joe breathed hard a few times, the two thugs in front of him thought he was having an anxiety attack because they were about to shoot him with the .38. They glanced at each other and smiled.

Joe felt the rumble of phlegm wad up from his upper respiratory tract and work its way up to his throat. The sound was like the rumble of a small semi truck's engine as it warmed up cold diesel fuel.

The two goons looked at each other, and then around for what might be making that sound. The one with the gun raised it. Joe fired off the gob with a burst of air straight into the face of the armed thug, then moved.

The round missed and Joe moved in close for the counter attack.

* * *

Dad and I often spent hours in conversation. I followed his analysis of problems and proposed solutions that we evaluated. We made estimations and evaluations of legal matters, people we knew and situations they faced, and compared these to challenges that I faced, or someone else we knew. His mind worked at rapid levels, and to accompany this, he was skilled in the expression of complex thought. Understanding how I thought, he was able to make complex ideas comprehensible, even to an eleven-year-old.

Then he would ask me my opinion, listen to me and then talk about the positives of what I had proposed, and the negative side. He would outline three solutions to the potential problems and we estimated the accuracy and deployable effectiveness of each strategy.

The time I spent with him prepared me for many lessons and assignments in life. I only knew that as it was happening, I was in awe of how smart he was.

When engrossed in a subject, the blackness of a summer night fell fast. Hours went by as we conversed and threw around ideas, and then developed them into a comedic sensation that had us laughing from our bellies.

On those nights I stayed with him in the park, we were unified, and I shared his outdoor isolation around a campfire, just outside the city.

I, too, was one of the outcasts.

Riverside Park was our favorite because we could walk back away from the city cop patrol that checked the park for vagrants.

If it got to be late, I accepted a jacket from him and lay down on the ground on the other side of his makeshift fire ring.

"If you ever get taken prisoner, make sure to eat all the food they give you, because you never know when you may get to eat again," he said to me over the fire ring.

The prospect of getting taken prisoner was unflattering.

"Like what? Rice and fish heads or something?"

"Yeah, rotten meat, moldy bread—stuff like that." The heated can of beans I was eating with a multi-tool from Dad's pack suddenly seemed pretty good. Dad was enjoying watching me eat that can of beans he had been carrying around. He was providing a meal and getting to feel like a father who could provide for his son.

He stole moments like that when he could.

I was pleased to allow that.

"What was it like to be shot at out at Richard's?"

"That was bad news. Those bullets tracked me across the couch as I dove for the floor."

"Was he trying to kill you or just scare you?"

I remembered Derrick Lawton looking at me though the binoculars in his yellow pickup truck.

"He was trying to kill me. There is no doubt about that—the murderous little shit."

"Do you know who?"

"I got a pretty good idea." Dad was leaning back on his pillow, his legs already under the wiry, wool, army blanket. He was headed for sleep. In moments he was out. This was the best gift to be given, I would realize later, the ability to drop right off into sleep and escape all the pressure he faced so elusively.

Later I wished for that gift a million times in my life.

I found the windbreaker that I used for a blanket and put my head on my shoe, then watched the fire snap a pine log and blaze on top along with a rotten birch log that turned to ash over the pine soon enough.

I listened to Dad snore and looked at the stars that shined so high above the fire light. The river was silent but I could feel the rolling black water moving past like a tip-toeing giant. I imagined what it might be like to live like this, with nowhere to put your head. No building around you to call home and no job. No prospect for a future and beset by crippling loneliness.

The haunted mansion loomed on the hill, the window-eyes looking down at me. My imagination loved this type of stuff. Yet, it felt like a presence had joined us around the fire. I sat up.

Lit by star and firelight, I saw the figure of a man step out of the tree line. The Chippewa Indian medicine man appeared with full headdress and tomahawk in hand. He walked out of the dark tree line, stopped, and turned to look at me. I blinked and looked again. The image turned into the outline of a birch tree with a twisted knot in it.

I waited for sleep and it came with the crackling of the pine log. The hiss of pitch mixed with the warm feeling of the burning wood on my face.

The cop came after I had finally fallen asleep. A bright beam of light shined in my face and the blue uniform took shape behind it as I woke up.

"You guys don't have permission to be here. The park is closed."

"I have nowhere else to be right now," Dad replied. "Can you let it slide and let us get back to sleep?"

"No. I can't do that. You guys have to move on." The cop's light moved over the gear, then all around the fire, looking for something illegal.

"It's not like we are bothering anyone," Dad asserted. "You had to walk back here to find us."

"The park is closed. Move on or get a ticket for vagrancy." The cop was older and had an air about him that he had seen it all before.

"Well, that's just great. I get shot at by a psychopath and I can't get the cops to do an investigation for the life of me, but here you are with plenty of time to screw me over when I have no place to go. We always have to mess with those who have nothing. You know you got a nutcase with a .22 running around shooting at people? That bother you at all?"

"I know about that incident. That's a Lincoln County matter, Pat," the cop answered.

Dad and I got up and began assembling his meager items so he could cram them into his backpack.

"So this is the way you treat the homeless? Kick them in the ass when they're down?" Dad hissed looking at the man.

"The park is closed, Pat. You know that."

When we had everything together, we poured water on the small fire we had lit. The plume of smoke gathered in the moonlight like a sacred closing ceremony.

I was incredibly tired and my feet felt like rocks that weighed a hundred pounds.

Dad turned to the cop and said: "There was a time in this country when people were free. Now the citizens are subject to levels of astounding oppression by law enforcement. America has become rampant with thugs. Law enforcement is a favorite tool of the oppressors to screw over the poor. And, we are easy prey, aren't we, Officer Lambert? This county is in trouble."

"Thanks for moving on," the cop said, like he had said it a million times. He walked back to his squad car in the parking lot.

"Treatment for the poor is never shitty enough," Dad declared. "They have to take it to a new level each time."

We walked the trail back to the bridge that took us into town. My watch read three-thirty in the morning. Dad walked slowly, his head down. I was tired and I could feel his dejection.

"Let me carry that backpack, Dad," and he let me take it from him. "Where will we stay tonight?"

Dad looked around at the early morning darkness.

"You should go home and go to bed. I will deal with this and find somewhere to go."

"We could go stay in the concrete tunnels at St. John's school. On the playground they have those big concrete tubes that kids play in. That would be a good place for us to sleep."

Dad took the backpack from me gently. "You go on home now. Go home and go to bed. A boy shouldn't have to watch his dad get run out of a park. Find me tomorrow and we'll get some breakfast. I have ten dollars that Father Jim gave me. But you run along now, Jamie." His tone was soft, tender.

We stood at the foot of the T.B. Scott Mansion hill for a moment and looked around at the dew-layered, early morning, surreal emptiness of the street. I said good night and watched him walk slowly down the quiet street in the moonlight with his backpack on. He was stooping forward. The few possessions he had were heavy tonight.

He was a man with a broken spirit. I watched my dad disappear around the corner. To anyone else, he was just a bum on the street.

I glanced up at the mansion on the hill, and stopped. A shadow moved behind a hemlock tree and I saw an Indian warrior sneaking toward me with a tomahawk in his hand. He moved from tree to tree without breaking a twig.

He wore moccasins with soft deer hide on the bottom, so he could feel twigs on the ground. He wanted my scalp with the thick black hair attached to it.

I froze and glanced aside. Dad was gone.

When I looked back toward the shadow, I saw only trees bathed in blue moonlight. I started to trot away, then broke into a dead run.

CHAPTER 14

The Ancient Mariner would not have taken so well if it had been called The Old Sailor.

Samuel Butler

In my notebook: The Saga of Gross Joe *continues…*

Gross Joe hated it when the client cried. Grown men were the worst.

Mr. Kraft was the high school principal. He had hired Joe to follow his wife and let him know if she was having an affair.

Joe watched the man bawl like a four-year-old girl. The photographs of his wife kissing the gym teacher were clear enough. The buff gym teacher even had his hand on her booby, as he pressed his mouth to hers in the snapshot. Joe had been dressed as a janitor in the school for a week before he could get that shot.

Then there was the second picture.

It showed Mrs. Kraft with long legs, a short skirt, and a tight sweater. She had shiny nylons that did something magic to her legs, enhancing their beauty. She was sitting on a park bench with the gym teacher, Mr. Flores, and again, they were kissing. Mr. Flores's hand was on her juicy booby again and his other hand was on her thigh, right above where the nylon ended and suspension strap was buckled to hold it up.

Mr. Kraft groaned out loud when he saw that one. He looked up from his sob fest.

"Is there any chance it's a mistake?" he asked.

"Mr. Flores is getting to second base right there. I think we know what happens from here," Joe said. He lit up a cigarette. He didn't like to smoke but he might need a big lugie for a defensive weapon.

"Second base! I've only gotten to third base four times in our eleven years of marriage!" Mr. Kraft blurted out in a broken dam of rage. Joe reached into his desk drawer. He hesitated at the bottle of Jack Daniels whiskey, and instead reached for the Old Grand-Dad.

He poured out three fingers of the brown fluid in a tumbler and offered it to Kraft, who looked at it and then up at Joe.

"Do you have any ice, Joe?"

"No I don't have any ice. This is an office, not a golf clubhouse."

Kraft took the glass.

"Damn, Joe, don't you have a clean class? There is stuff growing in this."

"Whiskey kills germs. You need the damn drink or not?"

Kraft looked like he was going to cry again, so Joe stood up next to him and lifted him out of his chair gently.

"Listen, I'm really sorry your wife is messing around with Mr. Flores, but you wanted to know and you do now. My expenses went over so you will be getting a bill from me at the end of the month for seven dollars and fifty cents. I appreciate it if you could pay it right away." Joe knew that was the cost of the new Styx album he wanted to buy from Merrill House of Music.

"I have another client coming in, so you have to beat it," Joe said.

"Where am I going to go?" Kraft asked, as he was ushered toward the door. Joe took the glass from him.

"Look, I'm not a headshrinker. I don't know, kid. You don't have to go home, but you have to leave here now. Go see a priest; he'll give you some good advice."

Joe closed the door, threw back the shot of Old Grand-Dad, and rested his head against the door. Maybe he should have studied harder in math class or something. He let the thought go.

Remember: Get my swimming suit from John Purcell's house. Bring mask, fins, and slippers next time I go swimming there!

*   *   *

Dad was the street lawyer now. The people with legal troubles sought him out. Always, he did his best to help them. The contrite, the nervous, the worried people came frequently to find Dad that summer. They showed up at Judy and Bob's house, asking for me. They wanted to know if I could get in touch with Dad. I asked them who they were and took down a phone number.

They were housewives facing eviction, or mothers worried about their son who had been charged with a felony. Sometimes it was men in despair—facing a divorce and not having any money for an attorney. They had heard of this man with legal tactics and ability, who helped the downtrodden and the poor, and they walked across the park directly to us, sometimes children in tow.

From his desperate circumstances, he gave messages of hope to those people.

He applied his problem-analysis skills. And he helped a client prepare for hearings. He told people what to say in court to represent themselves and advised them what forms to file.

He was prevented from representing anyone because he didn't have a law license; he had let it expire without renewal, having hated the game and wanted nothing to do with it.

When the situation looked to be full of despair, Dad advised people that nothing was hopeless.

"If we just keep engaging them, the other side will screw up. They're not that smart. People credit these dunderhead attorneys around here with more skill than any of them have. Trust me." About other attorneys or prosecutors, he said: "These guys are paper tigers. They can't stand up to a challenge.

"File this motion. Demand to see the record and the police report. Demand to see what they are hiding, and don't let them tell you that you can't. It's in the rules of discovery." He told a young man in a suit who was looking at a charge of drunk driving: "Look hard at what they have done, and what the other side is doing right now. We will always find them screwing up. Because mostly, they are incompetent."

But when they left, he was spent after a long consultation. He needed a nap to avoid a crash and I knew when to give him room and let him recharge.

* * *

In the notebook I wrote with really small print, "Ok, I could kiss Jenny Wilson, endlessly." I had started drawing a line through it, but had lifted the pen before I got to the statement.

Write what will stop your breath if you don't write.
Grace Paley

Richard Putnam strolled into the yard of Judy and Bob Weaver with a wave of good nature around him. His Sam Elliot mustache had handle bars wound up at the sides and his plaid snap-button shirt was clean and pressed. He wore a cowboy hat in the north woods, so he stood tall. His appearance lightened the mood.

He greeted us with kind words and handed Dad a white envelope. Written on the front was the title that Richard gave Dad—Wild Counselor. His payment for legal help, and in cash.

"That should make us square for drawing out a psychopathic killer on the loose who is hunting one of us," Dad said. We all laughed at the dark humor, to my slight astonishment. Richard made a comment that facilitated the humor, and I joined in as well. It was laugh time—we knew how to play the game, and we were funny. That medicine is what kept us alive and the marrow in our bones.

We rode the wave of hilarity as long as we could. It would end too soon.

Dad enjoyed the money and threw it around. He handed some to people who were broke. He put food in our house, took me to the movies, and bought me pizza. We laughed over the steaming tomato sauce and were connected in a childlike, playful spirit that we had toward the world.

Dad purchased a ten-speed bike and it changed his summer. The bike was a silver Trek with narrow tires and a book carrier on the back over the tire. It became his horse. He purchased saddle bags and loaded them with items from the backpack. A bungee cord stretched out and held down a book of Buddhism, a book on Tai Chi, a sweatshirt with the sleeves torn off, and a big pair of rosewood nunchucks.

Now, Dad wasn't walking, but flying to daily mass on his new steed. He leaned on it while having coffee in the park. The bike lay next to him when he read at the cemetery. He spent time oiling the gears, cleaning the pedals, and shining the ghost-gray metal piping.

We blasted around town in the summer days like bats looking for a cave. We rode through an overhang on an insurance building and made a game out of yelling movie lines as we passed beneath it, imitating John Wayne or Edward G. Robinson.

Dad and I played bike tag, racing through the blocks of houses or downtown city area. We pushed hard through the parks, and knew a trail to get into the Council Grounds State Park, where you didn't have to go past the ranger post.

By the Wisconsin River we caught our breath and watched a hawk fish perched on a rock in midstream. The shadows, the smell of pine, and the river air were all good for us, and settled our minds from concern.

I had a little, square, silver, Panasonic transistor radio that I taped with black electrician's tape to the handle bars and I recall flying down the streets with Dad to the music of Santana performing She's Not There.

"You see, when a teacher gives you an F, they are giving themselves the F," Dad declared. "They have failed to teach you the lessons required to pass this class. You are a student, there to learn and absorb. If you are not learning the subject, we must look at the credentials of the entire educational system and its success ratio, to see if there is a problem here." Then he pulled hard on his Marlboro 100.

"I think I see," I said, as an eleven-year-old. I liked this liberal philosophy.

"So don't let it bother you, that you are having trouble in school. I would expect that anything you do, you do to the best of your ability. Would you say that you are approaching your studies with that respect?"

"I don't know if I can say that." I realized then how I had been only mildly interested in school.

"Well, do you take work home to do in the evening and read the books they tell you to?"

"Not really."

"What are you talking about? You read books all the time."

"Yeah, but not textbooks."

"It is important that anything you do, you do the best you can. Do you agree?" Dad's eyes found mine from beneath the unkempt mop of hair.

"Yeah."

"And if you want to be a screw-off, that's okay. I live this lifestyle not so much that I am a screw-off, but because there is something wrong with me and I don't seem to be able to..." Dad took a deep breath. "...function. Do you understand?"

"Sure."

"No one plans on this shit happening to them. No one wants to be homeless. So do what you can do—the very best you can. Be grateful to God that you can do these things, and take them seriously."

"You have two college degrees and passed the bar exam. What did it get you?" I asked with a half-smile. This was risky. It could go either way. He laughed; we both did then.

The bike gave Dad a sense of empowerment and made him mobile, and that meant freedom.

When we biked around town, we had our favorite places to stop and eat a peanut butter and jelly sandwich. In the back of the cemetery, the church had created a monument to the unborn. We sat on the cool granite and discussed life, politics, oppression, and liberty.

It became a game to throw the knapsack back and forth between us as we rode through the streets.

Dad threw it back to me but too far ahead of my grasp. In an instance of dread, I saw it heading for my spokes. Everything that followed happened in a time frame of two seconds.

The army-green knapsack hit my front tire and twisted in the spokes. In a half-second, the wheel completed its revolution. It jammed up in my fork and stopped the bike dead from a thirty-mile-an-hour, leg-powered cruise of torque.

I launched over the handle bars and stupidly clung to them.

I landed on my head, then my side, and skidded along, dissolving on the pavement before coming to rest in a fog of pain. Stars of concussion flashed in front of my eyes. The world spun. I heard the sound of my bike slamming onto the road, then bouncing. My vision was a tilted camera.

The experience seemed to have no end or beginning. A strong aroma of vanilla filled my nose and I had an overwhelming sense of Déjà vu. I had felt this somewhere before, seen this, been here. The sensation spilled over my mind like a chemical yamaka. Then there was silence around me.

Dad's face loomed down at me.

"You landed right on your head!" he kept exclaiming.

I writhed in pain on the black top. The world tipped back the way it should, and I sat up slowly. I came back into my body from a position up above, near the top of a big, beautiful, oak tree.

"Time for damage assessment to commence," I heard a voice from an internal engine room deep within me. The vanilla was so strong I was becoming nauseous.

I had a large abrasion, four inches long, that stretched across my forearm. It looked like leftover lasagna. There was blacktop gravel and dirt in the open wound. My head dripped blood and gave me liquid-red Elvis chops.

Dad looked down at the open scrape on my arm and spit in it. The white foam of his gob landed in the abrasion.

"What the hell are you doing?" I yelled.

"It is to clean it. I saw it in a cowboy movie."

"That's how things get infected," I said in shocked amazement.

I lay on the street and Dad crouched next to me, wondering what he could do to help. We were in front of a house with big picture windows that faced the street. A woman came out of the house and walked directly toward us.

"Pat, you still owe twenty dollars for the steaks you ordered two Saturday's ago. Do you think you could pay that?" she asked. Dad looked stunned for a moment.

"What?" he said.

"You picked up some steaks and still owe us the money from them."

"Well, this is great. Here my son is hurt and you run out here, not to help, but to dun me for a bill. Have you been waiting for us to come by, hoping for a catastrophe so you could address the late payment for some steaks? What a great opportunity for you to collect. Forget the fact that my son needs an ambulance. What's really important here is the fourteen bucks I owe you, is that right?"

"We are a small business and trusted you to pay us back."

"There is a time to do this. This is not it!" Dad said in disgust.

I groaned. The woman walked away ending the strange, social standoff and I got up, moving an inch every second. My fingers reached out and worked the knapsack out of the spokes of my bike. My view of the world had the tilt to it again.

We rode off down the blacktop street in silence; the fun had gone out of the ride for me. I stopped and threw up in the middle of the street. The vanilla sensation filling my nose, mouth, and throat, burned like acid. I purged and felt some kind of pressure release in my head, then watched the dripping blood and bile from my stomach mix together next to my left shoe.

The mess pooled in the street and when I could breathe again, pedaled on, next to Dad. He rode beside me and didn't say anything, only watching me ride and struggle internally.

"You fell right on your head," he said twice as we worked our way to the other end of town, so far away.

CHAPTER 15

Blessed are those who mourn, for they shall be comforted.
Mathew 5:4

"I also expect my three sons to be able to use their minds enough to keep them out of one fist fight after another. You don't have to knock down every asshole that comes along; you would be knocking down assholes all day long."
Pat Finucan

"Sometimes your dad does not use very sound judgment. Do you understand that, Jamie?"
Mom

The Sound and the Fury *began with a mental picture.*
William Faulkner

The night before the fair was to begin, I stood in the yard watching the evening advance. A storm was in the air and the atmosphere was electric. I watched three thunderclouds converge on each other like dragons above Merrill. They swirled to become a face that changed from a smile to a scream and then a giant fist that opened to a rose.

I felt alive at a new level. I was acutely aware of who I was and what I faced.

The fair coming to town was sweet and bitter. The fun was in getting out, riding on rides, eating food, and seeing everyone in town traipsing up and down the midway. The bitter part was that everyone would be there, including my arch rival, Erik Krumel, and his diabolical goon squad. And they would be looking for me.

I watched the storm in the sky and felt what Krumel was thinking, and I knew I was right. He was thinking of me at that moment, with great hatred in his heart. I could feel it in the air.

We counted the days until the fair was on in town. Summer in Merrill was rich because of the swimming and fishing holes, the warm weather, and football and baseball games in the park, but the height of it all was the fair. We talked about the rides we wanted to go on. Discussed in great detail who had thrown up on the Zipper, who wimped out on the Rock-O-Planes, and what girl was kissed on the Ferris wheel.

In the early morning the day before the fair opened, we walked through the festival grounds and watched the transformation as the carnies set up their tents. They were an instant city of people from every walk of life—waking, shaving and towel-showering in the early morning sun.

They were grizzled and weathered gypsies, like us all, living day-by-day and running from something. This fascinating subculture had found a home together. I walked among them as they joked. We shared familiar ground. Some were grumpy. I imagined that the unhappy ones might be men who left behind children and a wife, and were like my dad, lost and bumming around on this ever-moving show.

I envied their subculture just then, and I would have loved to have been accepted there.

A man walked out from behind the pneumatic, BB gun range with a tooth brush, wearing dungarees and a sleeveless undershirt. I imagined my dad one of these men, finding a rambling home, talking about me, his kid back in Wisconsin.

The comparison stunned me. I had to move my feet faster to keep up with my friends.
We walked through the sounds of tent pegs being pounded, machinery being tested, and trucks idling. The smell of diesel engines spiked the air. In hours it would be different, with bells ringing, children laughing, rides running, and carnies calling out to take a try at shooting the BB gun into the center of the star and winning the big, stuffed gorilla that hung by a wire above the stand.

What girl could resist a kiss from a guy who had won her the big gorilla? She then had to carry it clutched to her side, working the ridiculously huge, stuffed animal through the crowds, people noticing she had the boyfriend who won her the gorilla.

Maybe this year I could win it for Jenny Wilson. That might take the chill from her perception of me. We left the park with the sun moving later into the sky, the tent city emerging behind like an un-trusted mirage.

Pete came over to my house in the morning. We met there to go to the fair. My step-dad was doing some work on the roof of the house and thirty feet of scaffolding was against the siding. Huge oak planks lay across the metal framework, which provided a set platform, allowing him to work high off the ground. Pete and I found it intriguing and climbed onto the structure.

We scaled up like spiders. I was going to yell something clever down toward Pete when suddenly I felt the scaffolding begin shifting away from the building. It moved slowly from the wall, at first, but picked up with gravity.

"It's tipping over!" I yelled and jumped down to the ground.

Pete jumped, hitting the ground after I did. We ran, trying to get out of the shadow of the massive metal rods and wooden planks. We should have run to the side, but we ran away from the threat. I managed to clear the scaffolding and turned to see Pete trip and fall within the range of the structure. The top oak plank chopped down onto his side, making him cry out and double up in response.

He pissed his pants immediately. He was crying and clutching his stomach for a long time. I said things like: "Man, that really hit you hard" and "It knocked the piss out of you." These were consoling statements at that age. He was a trooper and after about twenty minutes he was on his feet. The big, wet stain of urine on the front of his jeans reached all around his backside and down to his knee. He walked with a waddle, like he didn't want his wet pants rubbing on his skin.

"I'm going to get a rash. I should go home and change." He looked down in his pants. "It looks like blood."

After he came out of his mom's house with different pants on, he looked better, but something was still knocked out of him, and his playful sense was forced. The way he worked hard to have fun, even though he was in pain, was akin to character.

The fair grounds were alive with people from all ages and arenas of life. The warm breeze that moved over the midway smelled of cotton candy, caramel apples, and grilled burgers. A kid walked by me with a handmade corndog that dripped mustard and ketchup. The corn meal was browned to a golden glaze. The big, juicy, all-beef dog would be moist to the core.

People were lining up at the grandstand for a tractor pull, and girls our age were walking around in clumps smiling in the sunlight.

John Purcell double-stepped up beside us.

"There's Jenny Wilson," he said like he was looking at a Vargas girl drawing. She glanced at us and kept talking to her friend. "She is in gymnastics. She's so cute."

"Yeah," I acknowledged.

"You got it bad for her, don't you?"

We walked by a radio that was playing Paul Revere and the Raiders' "Kicks." The girls turned and walked right toward us. They were a squad of beauties, each with their own feature.

We all stopped in front of them, and they us.

"Hi Jenny," I said. She looked away.

"Does your dad sleep in the park?" Katie asked me. Now Jenny looked at me. I let it play out. "I heard he has no home and sleeps at night in the park."

"Yeah." I wanted to give her the finger, but we were in such a public place. I took the high road. I was the afternoon sacrifice. Sometimes it just worked like that.

"That's weird. Why doesn't he get a job?" Jenny asked.

"It's complicated," I replied. The girls laughed. I looked up and found a crow in a tree, and I praised God when it called out to me in a three-bleat caw.

"His dad is a bum," another girl said, and they laughed again. I let it play out and we walked away. I walked around the fair like Pete—like I had the shit kicked out of me. When we passed Jenny Wilson again on the fairway, she didn't look at me, and the girls with her snickered.

"You really let her get the best of you. Why didn't you say something?" John asked. I was no longer a giant in his eyes. "You guys are limping around here with your asses hanging out. If you don't start getting cool, I'm gonna find some new friends." He stopped at a game to throw darts at balloons that, somehow, magically moved when the dart just about hit them. But John's arm was faster than the wind and he won a Dallas Cowboys cap.

He was like that. He won all the time. He put the Dallas hat on right away, turned and smiled. The star on this head was some kind of halo.

"You look like Richard Dreyfuss," I commented, without knowing why. Nothing meant anything. We were eleven. Nothing was a big deal yet. We strolled on down the midway.

The big, fat, hand-rolled corndogs were consolation. We smothered them with ketchup and mustard, and chewed them off long, pointed, wooden sticks.

"Kummel's buddy, Ron Thompson, is here with his posse and they are looking for trouble," a classmate shared with us as he passed. Ron Thompson was a football player who liked to tackle people off the field, as well. His signature move was to blindside his victim when he was not looking, then straddle him for a ground-and-pound—that is, he sat on the chest of the victim and punched his face.

Thompson's last name aided people in calling him "Tommy Gun," because he hit hard and fast like the .45 caliber sub machine gun.

Ron was like Erik, two years older than us and big. There were rumors that when he had encountered Riley Jessup on Pier Street Bridge, he had punched him several times, then threw him off the bridge.

The water was just barely high enough to break his fall, but often it was low, and the thirty-foot fall could have been a death sentence. Ron Thompson didn't care. He was a heartless asshole. Riley never reported the incident to the cops. He didn't want to have any repercussions and was hoping it would blow away.

He had limped home, leaning on his trashed bicycle and feeling a mix of being lucky to be alive, against the internal damage of having been victimized.

I eyed the wooden corndog spike in my hand and decided against it as a defensive weapon. Sometimes it was wise to limit options to intended consequences. I didn't want to hurt anyone; I just wanted to have a nice time and then get home in one piece. I had that right.

We were on the Scrambler when they saw us.

Ron leaned on the small metal guard that kept people out of the reach of the swinging bench seat and watched us scramble in the air on the ends of mechanical tentacles. Five of his friends joined him and they stood talking. I knew they were waiting for us to get off. Pete and John saw it, too. The gang wore jean jackets with the sleeves ripped off and work boots on their feet.

The fun left the fair. In a moment, it had become a quest for survival, against odds.

Ron's homemade tattoo of a diamond flexed on his forearm. His face was covered with a scruffy beard with the type of hair that looked like it should be covered with underwear. When the Scrambler came to a stop, I knew why they were at the exit gate. We walked toward them like we were walking toward our doom.

Somewhere I still expected some rules of society to apply because we were "in public." That fell away when Ron stepped toward me just after I had walked past him. He connected with a punch to the side of my head that flashed stars of pain across my eyes. I doubled over and he grabbed my head. My only shot available was a groin punch and I took it.

It felt like it connected, but he didn't react. We swung at each other a few more times. He had the advantage of a longer reach, and as I stepped out, he caught me again on the nose with punch. I had moved with it just a bit, saving me from being knocked out.

The smell of black liquorish filled my senses right after the impact. Then the salty smell of my own blood.

But when we squared off, he held his ground and did not advance. His shoulders slouched a bit where they hadn't before. I hoped my groin punch was neutralizing the attack.

"The next time I see you, I will kill you," he said with a strain of pain in his voice. I pinched the flow of blood from my nose and threw down a splatter of it on the dirt ground. I remembered Spit's dirt clod. My nose was having a tough week.

His friends stood there, wondering if they should be punching my friends. They moved on and we stood there.

I was breathing hard and my ears were ringing. But I was left with something and I wasn't sure what it was. Certainly not victory, but we had not run. So maybe we couldn't, but we stood our ground and perhaps now he might respect me. The fair became a tournament of conquest.

Pete limped away from us to his house as we walked past. He sped up his steps to retreat to the safety of his Mom's arms.

John branched off his way. I made my way home. I had survived the first day of the fair. There was jubilation in that. I walked past a car with a radio on, playing "Dancing in the Moonlight" by King Harvest. But the nausea that always seemed to grip me after traumatic experiences threw saliva in my mouth, like a seashore waiting for a tsunami.

I purged on a neatly trimmed lawn. Bile blasted out of my mouth with fire-hose force and piled undigested corndogs on the green blades. A dog barked at me as I straightened up. The sound gave me a headache.

*   *   *

A few days later, my head still hurt and my neck was stiff. In the early morning summer light, I got on my bike and took off down the driveway to find the day.

I passed the grocery store and saw Derrick Lawton's yellow pickup coming to a stop. He sort of pounced out of the driver's side door, and I saw Gus's mark scratched down the metal. Trish got out of the passenger door. They walked into the store. Trish moved with a graceful confidence that captivated me.

In Stange's park, Dad was leaning on the bridge rail, looking down at the water. My head felt like it was double sized.

"I didn't see you in mass yesterday. Did you go to the ten o'clock?" Dad asked.

I picked up a rock that looked like it had been polished and rolled it in my hand.

"No. I didn't go."

Then I threw the rock into the Prairie River. It entered the water perfectly, like a rock always did.

"You missed mass on Sunday?" he asked.

"I did."

"Why did you do that?"

"I was tired. It was a nice day and I felt like relaxing in the yard with a cup of coffee."

"It's a commandment that you should honor God on the Sabbath. And, to you and me, that's Sunday. God has done much for you and has seen to your safety in many ways. You are very blessed. Aren't you?"

"I am."

"But you can't find an hour in a week to say 'thank you' to the most powerful force in the universe? You think pretty highly of yourself, don't you?"

"I didn't say that."

"Oh, but you do, by your actions. It is always our actions that tell what we cherish. You can't go around calling yourself a Christian and a Catholic if you don't go to mass on Sunday. Every Sunday, not just when you feel like it, but every Sunday. That's what we do." He lit up a cigarette. "Hey, kid, look at me."

I did.

"That's not too much to ask, is it? For you to show God that you are one of His by standing to be counted at Holy Mass?" Dad looked me in the eye.

"No, it's not."

"Good, I'm not raising a bunch of pagans," he said and flipped the pinched, white cigarette butt into the water, where it landed and floated down below us, beneath the bridge and on its way. I remember thinking: "Everything is on its way," as we walked out of the park.

We passed an automobile repair garage business with open doors. Two mechanics worked on a Mercury Sable in the open doorway. One of them looked over at Dad.

I felt a wave of aggression coming off him before he said a word.

"Hey, skid, quit smoking in the street!" he called with a wrench in his hand. The moment hit us both in a surreal slap. Had he just said that to us?

"Hey, buddy, you get paid to shoot your mouth off and to wisecrack to people walking down the street, or to fix cars?"

The guy hadn't expected this response.

"I'm just wondering what kind of business you're running here, 'we fix your car and cock-off to people on the street as we do it!'" Dad said with a cheerful dip in his voice.

"You believe this guy?" Dad said to the other mechanic. "He works for you?"

"I didn't say anything," the other mechanic replied. The moment wound and then unwound itself. No one moved.

We walked away down the street.

"You see, Jamie, how people treat you when you are poor? Did you get a load of that guy?"

The dejection was noticeable in Dad's posture and this would grind on his mind all day. There was nothing I could do about it now. But I saw he was right—he didn't get respect, and it was because he had nothing.

"Can you imagine having to deal with that shit and being sick on top of it? I got assholes trying to kill me, no one giving a damn, and I can't walk down the street with my kid without some punk lipping off. I hate my life," he added with a deflated voice.

I walked with him in the conflict of wanting to spend this day with my buddies, rather than my depressed dad. I thought of ways to escape into a different world, one where my head and neck wouldn't hurt so much.

* * *

Gross Joe moved just fast enough so it wouldn't look like he was running but the Chinese assassin stayed with him in the elevator of the Sands Hotel and Casino in Las Vegas. The elevator was packed with folks, a blackjack dealer, wearing a visor, and an Elvis Impersonator who glanced at Joe as he packed in with them.

Before the door slid shut, the Chinese assassin pushed his way in, too. Instead of staring at the mirror door, he just stood and glared at Joe with a smile. He wouldn't do anything in the elevator, not with a blackjack dealer on board. They stood staring at each other as the elevator lifted.

Joe had no choice. He let go one of his deadly farts, the one that sounded like a tuba playing a whole note for two measures. Joe was looking in the face of the assassin and saw his eyes widen in horror as he released it.

The other occupants of the elevator looked at him in the mirror in a mixture of fear and dread.

"Man, you got no heart," Elvis said. By the time the elevator got to the ninth floor, the door slid open and everyone crumpled and fell out onto the gold carpet. Joe stepped over them and made his way to his room. He had to get out of there fast.

The Chinese assassin lifted his head off the floor and watched Joe move away. He lifted a trembling arm to his face and spoke into a microphone attached to his shirt sleeve and said, "The target has escaped." Then he threw up on the plush carpet.

CHAPTER 16

He told the truth in order to see.
Gene Baro

Let's say that he (an apprentice) should go out and hang himself because he finds that writing well is impossibly difficult. Then he should be cut down without mercy and forced by his own self to write as well as he can for the rest of his life. At least he will have the story of the hanging to commence with.
Ernest Hemingway

The backyard boxing match of the summer occurred between my brother Shawn and a much larger opponent, Greg Hacker. Shawn was the oldest of us four. He stood a straight-up, five-foot-eight, stayed in shape, and spoke only when there was something to say. The thick, black mane trademark on his head was a crown of heat in the summer.

In high school, he had a few close friends, but was comfortable as a loner. On the pressboard wall of his basement bedroom, the Bruce Lee poster showed the master in his Kung Fu stance with the three cuts on his left pectoral.

The school year had been a difficult one for him as well. A student, who was bigger than Shawn, was hassling him in hostile confrontation. The bully experience is never pleasant.

But it can only be endured for so long. No one knows whose idea it was, but Shawn and Hacker agreed to a boxing match to hash out their differences. Scheduled two months out, it gave the fighters ample time to train.

He purchased several books on boxing that are in my library today. The movie Rocky had come out the year before and influenced us all. I remember the movie teaching me an important lesson about ambition, at an age when I needed it.

The Finucan-Hacker fight was anticipated by kids of all ages and even grownups who were boxing enthusiasts. It quickly got to be the talk of the small town.

Shawn had a part-time job flipping burgers at the A&W restaurant across the street. When he wasn't working, he ran, did push-ups, and doubled his time working the heavy bag. He let out a little hiss with every sting he threw to the bag. The sound took on a life of its own, like a monster awakened in the basement, rising and falling.

Shawn jumped rope in the yard wearing a heavy sweat suit and soaked it. He did pull ups with a twenty-pound weight strapped around his waist.

He changed the way he ate, drank goat's milk, baked his own bread, and ate homemade yogurt from a white machine that showed up in the kitchen.

In the evenings, he read books. His room was quiet and he would lie on his bed and read books on travel, hiking, and outdoorsmanship.

How the fight got to be set up next door to our house had to be Shawn's idea. The Department of Natural Resources building butted up against the small forest that I walked through to get to Blue Boats. Behind the stone structure built in the years of the Conservation Corp, back in the Great Depression, there was a clearing, free from all prying eyes, yet still in town.

When that Saturday arrived, people came from all over town. Teachers, kids, construction workers, farm hands, and laborers from the paper mill nearby started appearing. People I had never seen in Merrill strolled into the big yard, like they were arriving at a barn-raising.

There was an air of festivity in the faces and strides. I recounted an observation I had made: that girls made the front row of a fist-fight circle. They loved to see a fight.

My step-dad, Bob, noticed the young and old traipsing past his house like migrating spiders. The crowd milled about as the boxing ring ropes were set up. Bob walked through the crowd, moving against the human tide, with his hands in the air.

"There is nothing to see here. Everyone go home. This is private property." But people just moved around him. "There isn't going to be a fight here. You can all leave," he said aloud. But this fight was an idea whose time had come—a force set into motion.

I climbed up on a bright, red, steel trailer the size of a truck. It was a canister used to carry water to a fire. I had a visual advantage from my high position, and I could see the faces of the spectators as well as the fighters. The variance in ages was remarkable to me. There were kids I had seen at wrestling tournaments in the crowd.

Tim came with a team of friends. He looked intense. To Tim, this fight was about redemption of the family name and would give us a reason to hold our heads high in this town.

From my perch on the metal trailer, I could see Jenny Wilson, chatting with her friends, enjoying the tension and excitement. She was excited about the fight. At school, she was one of the girls in the front row of the fight circle. I recalled having been yanked out of a fight by a teacher, spun around by my hair, where I had to face the girls in the front row of spectators, and she was there with a deadpan look, biting her lip.

I would see those girls in class again. Some avoided my eyes. I wondered if it was because they watched me receive punches, or if I had knowledge of some dark secret.

My eyes moved around the crowd. I was mystified at the gathering.

People had come to see a resolution of conflict in some ways, the only way it can be worked out, in a sanctioned scrap. When the two fighters took their corners, the difference in size and weight was alarming. Shawn moved around in his grass corner and shook his gloved hands, and glanced over at the opponent. Greg Lyon was the official referee of the bout. He took charge and used his distinctive scraggly voice to make clear the rules.

He called them to the center of the grass ring to face off before the bout and gave them the rules; Hacker was smiling down at Shawn in arrogance. They clashed in the center of the ring.

Shawn knew how to box. To the degree that footwork allows an advantage, he had it. He moved in and out with some devastating combinations and circled away from Hacker's heavy right hand. And the right hand was heavy; Shawn was hit more than once with it.

Hacker breathed hard after a little while. Someone hadn't been doing their road work. Shawn held it together in the brawl for a long time. He turned his heel when he struck and pivoted his weight into his punches. Heavy hands, built on the big Everlast bag in the basement, moved the big, long-haired kid around the make-shift ring by the end of the third round, and he was breathing harder still.

Hacker wasn't smiling by the end of the fourth round. But neither was Shawn. The punches he was taking were diminishing his response time. Shawn was unafraid and committed to the outcome. But he charged into a series of right-left-rights that almost knocked him down. It amazed me how quiet a crowd of so many people could get. They waited to breathe.

Some called it a draw, and others said that Shawn lost. As we dispersed, I saw that Tim was proud of our older brother.

The crowd dispersed—abuzz. Around town and in the schools, it was a story of inspiration.

"No one is talking about Hacker, but everyone is talking about Shawn," Tim said in triumph.

The boxing match seemed to have set a stake in the ground for our family identity that was seldom challenged. It had been a demonstration of who we were as Finucans—not broken, homeless and poor, as Dad was, but a family of Irish kids who stood up for themselves. Shawn inspired us, and others who saw the fight, to believe in ourselves. Though his life was short, I often recall the lessons of gentle leadership he taught me by example.

* * *

"He had a concussion from that fight and lay in bed for two days!" Mom still says when the subject comes up.

A car went by outside the window of my Mother's house and it made the same hissing sound I heard growing up.

The smell of the paper was old and familiar to me.

I turned the page on the notebook, letting the memories of the struggles of that summer knock around in me like a hammer falling down an open elevator shaft—ringing out like a voice of an 11-year-old, reminding me who I was.

I imagined myself as that 11-year-old, walking down the stairs now, past me. He might glance at me, an old guy now, and say "hi," but be on his way—to adventure and fun. I might insist on him stopping, then give him a hug, tussle his hair, and tell him, "You're doing a fine job. The best you can with what you have."

The solace of the house fed me. I sat in the quiet rocking chair that was a part of my first memory—my Mom rocking me in this chair, singing in a beautiful voice:

Go tell Aunt Rosie, Go tell Aunt Rosie, Go tell Aunt Rosie

The old grey goose is dead.

She died in the mill pond, she died in the mill pond, she died in the mill pond.

I tasted life. There was something deliciously bitter in the painful nostalgia. This triadic sense of life, its powerful aroma, and stimuli. Is this what drew my dad into a black hole? The cars hissed by.

Sometimes when traveling through time, it's hard to come out of the tunnel. I missed my brother, Shawn, and my dad.

*   *   *

Dad and I were having fun riding our bikes around town. We ate sandwiches in the cemetery in the back of potter's field. Dad told me stories of Merrill when he was a kid, what he did with his friends for fun, and he told me about his dad.

Grandpa Jim had been a medic in World War I, where he had seen action in trench warfare and had been exposed to mustard gas twice. He graduated from Columbia University and opened his optometry office in Merrill in the early 1920's. Grandpa Jim suffered from post-traumatic stress disorder from the war and walked the streets of Merrill, sometimes all night.

"When they kicked me out of Notre Dame, they made my father cry. It was the only time I had ever seen him cry," Dad said, a little too tragically.

When we stopped on our bike trek through town to eat barbecues at the Dairy Queen, we watched people pass by in their cars and the kids walk up and down Center Avenue.

Sometimes we laughed most of the afternoon. The despair didn't find him if we stayed busy. The totality of his situation didn't bother him as long as we were having fun.

Dad looked odd to others in his shorts, t-shirt, tanned skin, and Raising Sun headband. His eccentricity was displayed in his dress style; how could it not be? We drew stares and glances from the good people of Merrill. As that summer wore on, I learned to care about that less. He was my dad, and I didn't care what people thought.

"That they think at all, is in question," Dad would remark.

Off Center Avenue, another place to eat outside was A&W, where Shawn flipped burgers. On the concrete tables by the street, Dad might pause as he walked to the table, and let out a fart while pretending to shoot a pistol to the sound. It embarrassed me, especially if friends and people were around, but I ended up laughing.

Sometimes, it was like hanging out with a big kid. To me, it was a blast to have my dad as my best friend.

"So the old man says to me, 'When I saw the bear, I went AAAAHH, and shit my pants.' I said to him, 'Well, if I saw a bear, I would shit my pants, too.' He says to me, 'No I just shit my pants when I said AAAHH, just now,'" the joke went, and he told it well. Then he bit into a Papa Burger.

When the afternoon grew long and dinner time approached, I would run home and get some food for us to share in the park. As the warm air changed to evening, Dad would lie back against the sturdy picnic table and begin to go down the dark alley of introspection.

When I had all I could handle, I took leave for the day. I knew when to shove off on my own. I hoped to find him tomorrow in a better place mentally.

As I left him to spiral in Riverside Park, he called out to me: "My dad used to say, 'don't meet yourself coming back on the road in life.'"

"What does that mean?"

"I'm not sure," he replied, with his last smile for the day.

* * *

When I walked into the house, I could smell medicine in the air. The living room had been transformed into a medical ward. Tim was stretched out on the couch, a bandaged, right hand elevated, draining puss from a tube.

He looked feverish and concerned to the point of despair.

"He got into a fight and punched someone in the mouth, and now it's infected," Mom related in suppressed rage.

A large laceration gashed across his right hand, opened by a tooth. The doctor had removed a filling from the back of his hand. The human mouth is rife with bacteria and shortly after the doctor stitched it up, it became dangerously infected.

The doctor had told my mom and brother that the hand may have to be amputated to prevent the spread of staff infection up the arm.

Tim was lying there in fever, dealing with the possibility of having a prosthetic hand the rest of his life. I sat down in the room to give support, but didn't know what to say.

"They are not taking my hand. No fucking way," Tim said in delirium.

His big, Casio diving watch lay on the coffee table next to the couch. My mom was sitting there offering encouragement. She was a pillar to us, always positive and supportive, sometimes with nothing but optimism.

"We'll keep on the antibiotic, take it easy and we can bring down the infection," she was saying.

After she walked out of the room, Tim turned his head and looked out the window.

"I just wanted to go to the depot and shoot a game of pool. I end up fighting for my life. Assholes are everywhere." He looked up at me and then down at his hand. He moved it so slightly and winced.

I didn't know what to say.

"If I end up with one hand here, the prosthetic better be a hammer, because there will be a lineup of assholes around the block to scrap with me." His fever sent him off to a fitful sleep.

* * *

Tim had been attacked, and injured, my homeless dad was fired on with a semi-automatic weapon by a psychopath who had looked at me through field glasses, and I had bully problems of my own around every corner. It was the summer of the hunt.

There were forces at work around us, things I didn't understand. But I began to see the energy differently and ask myself how I could imaginatively use these forces to counter what was taking place in our lives and to our family.

I wanted to gain an understanding about how to use forces at work, and not fight them. But for this, I had no master to teach me.

* * *

Crazy Daze in Merrill is a time of sidewalk sales and food. If the weather is hot, the merchants put out tables and sell products that are dated, or overstocked, at ridiculous prices. There is a circus aura to the day, and a promise of fun if you run into the right people.

The main streets are barricaded off so the city's main street becomes an outdoor mall. Hotdogs and brats are for sale; chili cheese fries and pizza are slung from a dozen stands.

That summer, a dunking tank offered a chance to drop the chief of police into the water. Pretty girls from the cheerleading club were selling cotton candy and corndogs. The famous Merrill City Band played big band favorites at the end of the blocked-off street. I recognized "In the Mood" by Glen Miller. The sound rolled down the street, an audio fog of nostalgia.

The mayor's dog, an old golden retriever with gray whiskers and a constantly wagging tail, moved around gently in the crowd, finding scraps of dropped food and handouts.

A baby cried over its mother's shoulder while she awkwardly pushed a stroller with another child in it. Beside them, two farmers in flannel shirts shook hands and greeted each other as old friends. They talked quickly until one roared with laughter.

John and I moved through the crowds, part of the spectacle. I felt the ion charge of energy and a feeling of community. I belonged here. I knew some of these people and was connected to them. This was the tribe that I was assigned to. In ancient times we banded together for the hunt and fought off enemies.

This was my town.

Jenny Wilson was with some of her friends. One wanted to talk to John. They stopped beside us.

"The pet store has puppies out in a little pen. Let's go look at them," I suggested to her. She looked away. Last year she and I had done this.

"No," she said in a frosty tone.

"She doesn't want to talk to you," Francine sneered. "She has the affection of enough poor boys." Then she fanned herself like a southern belle.

"You're eavesdropping," I replied.

"She wants a boyfriend whose dad has a job and a home," Linda taunted. They laughed.

I tried to catch a direct look into Jenny's eyes, but she turned away. I wished her friends were suddenly lifted away by giant crows.

Then I looked away. Trish Lawton was in hearing distance and watching. Her big, soft eyes locked onto mine. I saw compassion and understanding that stunned me.

"My dad says I can't see you. My dad saw your dad walking down the street and told me that," Jenny said, dismissing me and walking away. Her friends followed her like Chickadees, chattering and laughing. John had been silent.

I looked for Trish Lawton, but she had moved on, out of mercy.

"Why did you let her talk to you that way?" John asked

We moved down the street past three dancers dressed as mimes, dragging something invisible and heavy down the midway.

My feet fell hard on the ground; it seemed I could only move in slow motion. With each step, shame shook off me like corn flakes and left a trail, detectable by only the nose of a bloodhound.

"Come on, let's get a caramel apple," John suggested, tapping my chest, bringing me partially out of the abyss.

I was half-way through the sweet, green apple, covered in caramel, when I saw Ron Benson and Craig Wynn coming down the fairway. They seemed to feed on the energy of people around them as they walked. They stayed close beside each other, each step nosing ahead of the other for a moment in a competitive display of testosterone, shoving smaller kids in front of them. Benson was walking with his chin out before him, like the prow of a ship breaking waves. His head turned back and forth, looking for…trouble.

A feeling came over me that fate was pointing her finger at me. I knew a collision course had been set for this day.

Benson and his crew were scruffy, greasy, and unkempt—by choice and nature. They projected rejection of norms and etiquette, including basic hygiene. Ron had on a t shirt that said 'Phuck You' across the front.

Ron slammed into a sixth grader who spilled a Coke in a wax paper cup all over an old man wearing bib overalls next to him.

Craig Wynn was beside him and said something to a kid as they passed. The kid looked away.

"Heads up," I called to John. The boys were two years older and bigger than us. They closed the distance of the last few yards between us and then stood like a wall in our way. Even grown-ups moved around them.

"Wynn has it out for me," John whispered.

"No, Krumel put it out for me," I countered.

Wynn went right at John.

John Purcell's primary weapon was his speed and agility. Craig Wynn made a run at John, who watched his approach, held his nerve, and stood still.

I had seen John execute this maneuver many times, but each time he did it, it always astounded me. The technique was developed at a football game in his grandpa Romie's double-lot yard, when a football game turned into a game of "smear the queer." John Purcell used forces. He didn't fight them.

John took off fast. Wynn pursued. The chase went for about fifteen feet. Then John dropped down into a crouch on the ground and covered his head with his hands. Wynn tripped on John and flew through the air. His arms did a winding motion as he tried to keep his head from breaking his fall. He landed on the pavement, skidding on his face, with his legs splayed out above him.

Wynn got up faster than I would have thought, a scab of road rash on his cheek.

"Purcell," he said in astonishment.

People all around us turned to look.

John took two steps toward me.

"I got him with this same trick the last time he came at me at the lanes. How fucking stupid is this cat?" John said and crouched as the attacker came in.

Purcell sprinted off, but faked hard to the left, then went right to change directions. I knew what he was doing; he wanted to bring Wynn past us. Wynn had closed the distance and was reaching out to get a hand on the prey, when John dropped down into a ball on the ground. Wynn tripped hard on John's crouched figure. I saw his face as he flew past me; self-loathing at his own stupidity is what I read.

Wynn sailed headfirst through the air, his feet far behind him. He smashed into the booth staffed by the Democrats and broke a leg off the flimsy card table. The big woman behind the booth screamed and stood up. She shook her hands before her in terror and jiggled in her red-and-white polka dot dress.

John got up and watched Wynn, then moved back toward us with some side steps, like one of the Jet's in *Westside Story*. Wynn gathered himself in humiliation and painful fury. He did what we all knew he would do—run at John a third time. And John got him again. On the third fall, he was slower at getting up, and by the time he had found his feet, we knew the fight was out of him.

Nobody wanted to see it anymore. It almost wasn't funny. But then I remembered what a bully asshole he was; yeah, it was still funny.

Benson clobbered me twice before I could figure out where he was. His first two punches struck the side of my head while I was watching John take apart Wynn.

The third punch missed, because I had started to respond. My judgment was slow. But sparring told me to hold my hands up. The next flurry bounced off my arms.

I recovered in those moments and the fury lit. My opponent had attacked me when I was looking the other way. He was a coward. He needed a lesson in humility and I could help him. It would be fitting to come from me, an underclassman.

"Use your karate on 'em!" John yelled from the sideline, and got a roar of laughter from someplace far away.

The fog cleared. I moved in, remembering the karate class and being picked apart by so many taller, bigger students. "Collapse the distance to equalize the advantage."

I closed in fast with what I had. It seemed a bad idea at first, sort of like swimming out through surf, but once I got past his guard, I threw a punch. It landed on his thin, skin-covered skull. I had to take the fun out of it for him. I rocked inside, throwing left-rights with my heels pivoting on the ground. The energy I threw came from my hips.

I thought of Shawn's example and believed in myself.

Shawn's leather, Everlast, heavy bag was sixty pounds of hard stuffing. In the basement, I could rock it with punches, creaking the rafters in the floor, like my older brothers. Moving into the strike zone of a larger opponent seemed absurd, but it worked.

Our exchange was, at first, mutual in punches, but my hands were heavier when they landed, taking toll on him fast. He retreated a few steps; so did I, wanting only a graceful out for all. He did not advance. And that was all I wanted.

Someone yelled: "Hey, you damn kids, knock it off." John and I walked away down the midway, trying not to run.

Later I learned that the flurry of punches we had exchanged left Benson with a broken collarbone. I lost no sleep over that.

I thought of my brother with his torn-up hand, and my dad rolling across the floor of Richard's house, barely escaping a deadly, armed assault. I thought of Shawn, fighting in the make-shift ring behind the DNR building, and the massive difference in size of the opponent he faced, and how bravely he fought.

This summer I was learning what it was like to wear my last name in this town. And Dad was right—fuck 'em. From Tim, I was learning something about channeling rage. I learned that if you stood up to an asshole, they weren't that tough.

That night, the pain in my neck and throat woke me up every time I turned on my side. At three in the morning, I went outside and sat in the yard on the picnic table with my blue notebook. The moon was bright enough to see a shadow. I sat there bathed in the blue, summer moon and wrote:

Gross Joe looked at Frank Guts, his old ex-partner.

"What does that mean, 'I'll help you out, and you can count on me.' When you say that, what the hell does that mean?" Frank looked confused and drew on his cigarette.

"What the hell are you asking me, Joe? It means, 'I'll be there for you.' Like if you get busted for drunk driving, I'll come and bail out your sorry ass. It don't mean I'm not gonna help you bury a body, or help you fake your death or some shit," said Frank Guts.

"And quit smoking. You make this place smell like shit." Joe took the long cigarette out of Frank's mouth and threw it on the ground. What the hell would you want to see what you are breathing for?" Joe took his .38 revolver out of his pants and checked it.

"And comb your fuckin' hair. You look like a clown. What are you gonna do—jump out of a cake? Look, we're going in here and I'm gonna ask some questions about Louie the Lip. You just stand there and act tuff."

"Fuck standing here, I am tuff," Frank Guts said. He was a Green Beret in Vietnam, and Joe knew him to be a good guy in a scrap.

* * *

My penmanship was free and wild, outside the confines of the faded, blue ink—loose to create. Margins were a suggestion. I thought of the arthritis I felt as I grabbed the pen today.

Beneath my Gross Joe saga, I had drawn a pen portrait of a girl, who looked like Trish Lawton. The rough etching had caught the expression Trish had when she saw me get laughed at in front of Jenny Wilson and her friends. She had shared my dread, and therefore had somehow lessoned mine. Trish Lawton didn't like the blood.

* * *

Clouds moved in and covered the brilliant moon, making it too dark to write. I listened to the hiss of a solo car moving past on Center Avenue. I went inside and took two aspirin for my throat and finally fell asleep.

CHAPTER 17

"Remember, no matter what happens to you in life, when it feels like you can't go on and the burden of your life is too heavy, get some rest. It means that you need to get some sleep and things will be bearable in the light of a new day. And don't get too discouraged in life. The only thing that matters through this entire facade is your relationship with God."

Pat Finucan

Dad and I sat around a small campfire in Riverside Park. We burned small, birch logs that shown bright, but offered little warmth, and consumed themselves fast. Dad was gently settling into his campsite. We were deep in the park, away from the parking lot.

I poked my stick into the fire and felt the heat of the birch log on my front and the slight chill of night at my back.

"It hurts every time I have to swallow spit," I moaned. "I didn't know I had so much spit in a day."

Benson had landed a punch to my throat—one of the glancing blows that didn't register until later. The punch had bruised my esophagus, and every time I swallowed I felt intense pain, which challenged my psyche and left me feeling constrained.

"You have to learn to keep yourself out of fights. What the hell is it with you kids? Every time I talk to one of my sons they have just been in a fight. Do you know how to reason, to communicate? I mean, do you think you can just go around from one fistfight to another without consequence?" He looked at me, waiting for it to get through my head.

"I didn't raise a bunch of Neanderthals. Use your intellect. You are very smart, Jamie. Smart enough to keep yourself out of these fights."

"Yeah? Well, every time I turn a corner, some asshole is looking for a scrap with me, and I don't seem to have much choice in the matter as it unfolds. Do you think I like this shit? All I'm trying to do is have fun with my friends."

"I expect of you, the ability to keep yourself out of situations that..." Dad was saying.

"I didn't have much chance. He was opening up on me. I was looking away from him. The fucking pussy couldn't even look me in the eye before he unloaded on me. What the hell do you expect me to do? Negotiate with him as he's punching my head in?" I was yelling over my sore throat. I was close to tears.

We both let the silence of the night settle over us and I poked the stick in the fire. It turned over a log and the black side changed to red and glowed until the fire danced up onto it.

"Oh. Well, I'm glad you kicked his ass then. The son of a bitch had it coming."

"I stopped him. But the throat punch is killing me."

"Life is full of pain, Jamie—big pain, little pain, emotional pain, physical pain. Some pain you can't even understand, but it's there. To live is to negate the pain. Do you understand what I am saying?"

"Yeah, you don't want to hear me complain. I get it."

"No. I am trying to teach you something important. Pain can be an indication that something is wrong, or it can be a powerful force that drives you mad. It can make you crazy if you don't figure out how to read it and diagnose it. I live in tremendous emotional pain, all day sometimes. It can drive a person crazy."

I moved the stick in the fire. The coals sparked and then went black when they cooled. The warmth that emulated from the fire felt good against the chilly summer night. A summer storm front was moving in and there was electricity in the air.

"It robs you of peace, tears at your solitude, and blinds you to the needs of the people around you. Pain makes us self-absorbed. It can lead us into thinking we are the center of our world and nothing lives or exists outside that gray, painful world."

"Hmm," I mused and pulled the stick out of the fire. It had a little blazing flame at the end of it. I drifted off. I imagined swinging the flaming stick around in an arc to hold off the snapping jaws of hungry wolves that had moved in around us.

When I spun in one direction, the jaws of another gray wolf jumped at my back, just missing me as I moved. "Get back," I yelled. In the fire's glow, they advanced around me. A growl of hunger droned in the darkness behind yellow, reflective, eyeball lenses. I held out a torch and jabbed it at the advancing white fang in the orange light. The flames at the end of my stick flared in the motion. But they began to flicker and fade…

"Hey, did you hear me?" Dad asked.

"I heard you."

I put the stick back in the fire. The coals seemed to reach out to it and reclaim it. My Adam's apple moved and I winced.

"When you accept it, God can speak to you. Sometimes he uses pain to get through to us."

I didn't want the lecture tonight and he picked up on it.

"And one thing you need to know, is that we all need rest, and a good night's sleep to deal with it." Dad lay down on the ground and pulled his thin, wool, army blanket over him. His ten-speed bike leaned against a tree in the rim of the firelight, like an obedient horse.

"And right now, I am going to sleep. You should go on home and go to bed. You have things to accomplish tomorrow. Don't be a screw-off, or you will end up like me, sleeping in the park with nowhere to go and no one to care about you."

I left the dark park. The night air tasted of wet pine and my throat pain distracted me from solace. The empty streets of Merrill were lit up with lights but looked vacant, giving it a movie-set look. I walked home, feeling anguish that I didn't understand.

But soon enough, the vanilla taste filled my mouth and the doorway of my imagination opened. Highly trained members of the Triad began moving out in front of me, to intercept. They wore suits and sunglasses—the Triad guys always did. A tall assassin stepped into the street light's glow, staring at me. He settled into a deep Isshin Ryu stance.

His attack came in low, drawing his power from his hips and the earth. My Tae Kwon Do style was to attack high then, leaving the earth in a jumping kick, if I dared. I needed momentum. I ran toward the assault, stopping to spin-kick an attacker from my flank, wielding a heavy pair of nunchucks. I was able to dispatch the three who descended upon me, sustaining only slight injury.

The empty streets came alive with enemies as I ran. The heavy Samoan sumo wrestler, who sometimes appeared, charged me. I side stepped and connected with a back-spinning kick that sent him into a counter spin in the opposite direction. He lifted off the ground and rolled 360 degrees in the air before he crumpled to the ground.

Though there was no one on the streets of the small town, in the night air I suppose I looked nuts--kicking and jumping around, fighting imaginary opponents. But with no one out, I didn't care. I was dancing like no one was watching.

I was starting to care a lot less about what people might be thinking.

* * *

The rumble at the Crazy Daze was the event of the week in the kid underworld. People asked John and me how we took on two members of the Krumel Crew and managed to come through unscathed.

"I heard you left them on the ground," Bennie Schemlin spoke up. I told this to Tim.

Tim had been giving me a boxing lesson, and paused from stinging the bag to turn to me.

"When the scrappers hear that you are applying to join their ranks, they line up to give you a try," he warned.

John and I went to Blue Boats that Saturday. We started out walking on the wooded trail but it turned into a race. The trail passed in a blur. At one point, when it traversed along the ridge of an old sand pit, we ran side-by-side until we tried to push each other down the thirty-foot sand embankment.

When he got a few feet ahead of me, I stepped over double-fast and kicked his legs. My foot ended up connecting with one of his legs—Trip Time! He piled up at full speed on the sand trail, like he had been blindsided by Roger Staubach.

I laughed so hard it slowed me down, for John was the master of this kick-the-leg tactic and deployed it often. It was right and good that it should return to him.

When I made it to the corner that offered a view of Blue Boats with the water and rope swing, I stopped. There were three, pretty girls swimming. They were giggling, and screaming, and jumping off the big root that edged over the shoreline.

John's feet pounded to a stop beside me.

One of the girls was Trish Lawton. The contrast of her dark skin stood out on her white bikini.

I remembered how her dad was yelling at her when John and I were spying on her house. When I thought of that, a tinge of shame touched me.

We swam with them and played nice, like kids who haven't developed to the point of being consumed with adult unbridled passion. I measure an activity by how much laughter is had. With the hilarity meter running high, the afternoon passed too quickly.

The girls toweled off in the sunshine and slipped on sandals. I remember being mystified by their soft, skin texture and slight curves.

"Can I walk you home?" I asked Trish.

"I have some reading to do," she answered.

I picked up one of her books.

"*Huckleberry Finn*. This is one of my favorite novels."

She took the book back from my hand, but gently.

"I see myself as Huck Finn, if you want to know the truth. I could build a raft, head right down the mighty Wisconsin River, and get out of this dump." I was quoting something I heard my dad say. She was smiling now.

"Sure," she replied.

We walked past the pine trees on the sandy path. The other kids faded away.

When we arrived at her house, I glanced at the hedge that John and I had hidden behind to spy on them. I felt like a zit.

"Do you want to come in?" she asked after glancing around and making sure the house was empty. She was managing the shame of the dysfunctional family.

The house was clean but disorganized. Hunting and fishing equipment leaned against the walls and the furniture bore large, cigarette burns. A small desk was in the corner of the living room where Trish did her reading.

She showed me pictures she had taken with a 35 millimeter camera. They were laid out in a photo book, and many of them were stunning. I saw a picture of the clock tower in town, with sunset light beyond it, that gave me a new appreciation of the historical monument. Another photograph seemed to caress an image of a shaft of light on the mist of the river, with a big crow posing in the foreground. I looked at another—a sunrise on a pasture with cows drinking from a cowslip, the colors brilliant and clear.

I turned a page and saw a picture of myself, sitting on top of a picnic table at the Council Grounds state park. I was staring at something with a pensive expression. She had centered the shot to include a reflective light off the Wisconsin River, but I was clearly the subject of the photograph.

"Hey," I whispered in soft surprise. Trish leaned over and gently closed the book. She filled my senses with the lavender smell. A crimson blush graced her face, which was close to mine, and when we looked at each other, I saw unflinching confidence in her dark, brown eyes that stunned me.

"My dad will be home soon. You should go. I have swimming lessons tomorrow. I'm done at the pool at ten. Will you walk me home?" She moved to gather some things, but her brown eyes with green flecks locked on mine, and I felt the tug 'that never lets go' take hold.

She wore an expression that hid nothing. She faced life. If this girl gave you her heart, she would never take it back.

She hit me "like a drink of punch on a hot raft," Gross Joe would have said.

"Sure," I responded. She walked me through the house to the door. I saw the .22 rifle, which leaned behind the door. It was a Ruger, classic 10/22 style. My brother Tim had one just like it. This was the weapon he grabbed when he saw John and me outside his window—the one he most likely ran across the field with, in a low crouch by moon light, to shoot at my dad. Then had run back to his yellow pickup truck, until he switched to cool, wide strides after an attempted murder.

Trish was watching me look at it.

"My brother has one of those," I noted and stepped over to the rifle. I picked it up, pointing the barrel up, and opened the chamber. A brass casing was seated in the barrel, the primer unpunched. I could tell by the weight that the clip was full. My heart double-pounded as I handled the weapon.

My finger went to the safety. It was not on. The moron kept the weapon loaded, with one in the chamber, and the safety off.

I snapped on the safety, then shouldered the rifle and looked down the barrel, pointing it up, keeping my finger out of the trigger guard.

"Nice rifle," I commented. I moved to lean it back in the corner and, as I did, I noticed a coffee can on the floor next to it. It contained some .22 shells, live rounds and some spent cartridges.

I bent and picked up two of the spent shell casings. I rolled one on my fingertips. The brass had the extractor marks on the side of the shell, like the one I had found outside Richard Putnam's window. I froze in horror. Outside a crow cawed.

"What are you doing?" Trish asked.

"Sorry, I have shiny object syndrome. If I see something that makes me think of something else, it's like my mind takes a walk down this trail ..." I tossed one of the casings back into the coffee can, a brass-on-tin sound rang out. I slipped the other shell casing into my pocket.

She leaned forward and kissed me on the mouth. The sensation collided with my discovery. The smell of her perfume wafted over me and left me swirling. Her mouth was wet and hot. She opened her mouth and our tongues kind of met somewhere between our lips.

She pulled away and looked at me with a smile. Trish rolled her eyes and led me out the door.

"That was for helping me with my suitcase. That was so sweet. You have to go; my dad will be here soon." Her hands moved over my shirt, straightening it, smoothing it over.

"Can I meet him—your dad?" The question startled her. Her hands stopped and pulled away.

"What? Why would you want to do that?" I saw a flash of mistrust in her eyes. I felt the empty shell casing in my pocket.

She let me out. I moved slowly past her in the doorway. Then I moved toward her. She pulled away; I felt a tinge of devastation. I walked home but couldn't relax enough to get the vanilla taste.

*　　*　　*

I sat in the quiet house that I grew up in on that moody Sunday, listening to the traffic go by, and saw the same light through the windows that I had as a kid. It seemed I could touch the past, or that it was all the same—past, present, future—as if it were separated by a broken line somewhere.

I turned the faded, blue-lined page of the notebook and found a Bit-O-Honey wrapper pressed between them. I smelled the sweetness of childhood.

I read: "Get fishing line and bobbers!" (Beneath that a stick figure standing in a trout stream, casting a line far away like a dream.)

Then the *Saga of Gross Joe* continued:

"You just gotta help me, Joe. I need to know who killed my husband," Jenny Wilson said.

"I tried to help you before, Jenny, but my services weren't good enough for you. And right now, not that I think that you care, because I know you don't, I got problems of my own."

"You do? The legendary Gross Joe has problems?" she answered with a snide smile. Her eyes were still damn pretty. In her dress and heels, she looked hotter than the fudge on a banana split. She lit up a cigarette.

"There's no smoking in here, Jenny. Smoking is for losers, and yeah, rich, hoity-toities can be losers, too. Bet you didn't know that." A fly landed on the window and Joe spat a gob of phlegm that stuck it to the glass.

"Ah, Joe, don't you think you are being hard on me?" Jenny asked, moving closer to him. "If you do this for me, I could let you get to second base," she offered with a subtle smile. She touched his hair with her smooth gentle hand.

Joe thought to himself… Hmmm.

Beneath that, the schedules for the remaining baseball games at the ball park were written in fast hand.

"Remember to get Chris to tell me exactly where he caught the Brook Trout in Stanges Park and go back to that spot!"

* * *

Judy and Bob's house was an environment that could turn active quickly when the two adults were at work and we kids were around during the summer.

Deirdre liked rocking in her chair when she wanted to think. She had an Aerosmith album with her favorite song on it, "Dream On," and she listened to it over and over again while rocking and singing along with it. Her eyes were wistful with a far-off dream that only she could know.

Dad rolled into the driveway on his bike with the grace of a crow, leaning over the handlebars with his hands on the brakes. He looked like a mellow version of Peter Fonda in *Easy Rider.* He had the appearance of a creature of the summer from living outdoors. His skin was tanned, his shorts sprouted holes, and his hooded sweatshirt had the sleeves torn off. A bandana on his head featured a Japanese red sun. On the book carrier, a bungee cord held down a book on Zen philosophy, some Tropical Sun suntan oil, some vitamins, and his nunchucks across the top of it all.

After greeting me, he walked as though he was going to pass me, only to throw a surprise, fake-attack karate chop at my neck. "Hiyaaa," he cried out.

I went with it, pretending to be hit, and countered with a flurry of punches, then jumped back and mouthed words, but spoke only a few.

"Your Kung Fu is wushu," I laughed, "…and you have no spirit."

Dad cracked up and walked into the house.

The summer air smelled of the pine trees, an aroma that is the smell of the soul of summer.

"I have been taking these vitamins and I feel great. Most people don't get enough vitamin B12 and their immune system suffers as a result. Take some of these, Deirdre," Dad instructed, holding out the bottle.

"Here, take a bunch." He poured a handful of the green, vitamin gel capsules into our open hands.

"We're supposed to take them all?" she asked.

"Sure, look." Dad started popping the vitamins and washing them down with a glass of water with Foghorn Leghorn on it. The three of us swallowed about ten of the big, green capsules with lots of water.

"Sure. They are good for you," he said. "Your body needs this and doesn't get enough of them."

We set our glasses down, Deirdre went back to listening to Aerosmith and rocking in her chair, and I sat down at the table. I was waiting for the effects of the vitamins to make me feel great.

About fifteen minutes later a growing wave of nausea moved me out of my chair and toward the backyard. My mouth was filling up with a flood of saliva and I was thinking I needed some air. Deirdre passed me in a hurried step. Her face was as green as the handful of pills we had all taken.

She must have had the same idea—fresh air. We circled in the yard like dogs looking to squat. My stomach emptied first. Green bile painfully blasted out of my mouth and nose. It piled up on the lawn as I retched from the core of my essence.

Deirdre was right behind me, shaking her hands up-and-down while throwing up the same color of stomach bile. Together we emptied ourselves onto the lawn. Dad watched the spectacle with a mixture of concern and horror.

I immediately felt relief and walked back into the house. I needed to lie down.

I was learning a lesson: Dad's affinity for extremes could be dangerous. It is prudent to question authority. Also, throw up in the toilet, where you can flush it away, and not in the yard. Nothing disappears just because it is outside, even if it is organic material.

* * *

Pete was walking toward me on the street, limping. His gait was off, and the trademark Bucky Badger baseball cap on his head dipped with each step.

We were going to the Cosmo, the local movie theatre, to watch *Breaker, Breaker*, a new Chuck Norris movie. Pete cradled his left arm close to his body. When he got nearer, I saw the black eye and the fat lip. He avoided my eyes. His had a broken look.

"Erik Krumel beat me up yesterday," he explained, answering my question before I could form it. "He beat me up and I wet my pants. I couldn't help it. He kicked me in the stomach with the big, steel-toed boots he wears, and I pissed myself in front of a bunch of people; some of them were adults. None of them did anything. Everybody just watched."

"Where did this happen?"

"In the parking lot of Holiday gas station. He saw me in the store. Then he, Benson, and Wynn waited for me outside. I saw them notice me. I knew they would be waiting outside."

Moments passed with neither of us speaking. I just felt bad for Pete. He was a nice kid, not a scrapper to begin with. He had been preyed upon.

"Benson and Wynn stood there and laughed. They thought it was funny. Krumel was fast. He punches so hard I couldn't stand up anymore. I took a few swings, but his reach was so much longer than mine." Pete touched his front tooth with his turned up thumb, like it might be loose. "I couldn't get close to him."

I remembered watching Krumel get into a fight at a wrestling meet in Antigo. He had darted in fast and punched hard, bombing the other kid until he fell face-first onto the asphalt. The kid twitched as he lay next to the yellow bus from Abbotsford School district.

Erik Krumel went for the knockout when he smelled blood. He was long, lean, and fast—a deadly combination. Pete was not even in his league. And, technically, I wasn't either. These guys were football giants.

"Before he walked away, he told me to tell you that you're next." There was just a hint of blame in Pete's eyes, or maybe the tone.

I looked at the damage done to this kid and the rage lit inside.

"Let's go see Chuck Norris kick the crap out of some ass wads."

"Didn't he get his ass kicked by Bruce Lee in the last movie?"

"Yea, but come on, that was Bruce Lee."

"Yeah, it would be an honor to get my ass kicked by Bruce Lee. Not some fucking loser, like Krumel."

We laughed. Pete was going to be all right.

"Did you know that when Chuck Norris does pushups, he doesn't push himself up, he pushes the world down?" Pete said.

"Sure, and tears from Chuck Norris can cure cancer, but he never cries, so there is no cure for cancer."

"Chuck Norris once defeated the entire North Korean Army, with his penis."

"Once, someone asked Chuck Norris what his favorite song was, and Chuck Norris round-kicked the guy in the face until he started screaming for mercy. Then Chuck Norris said, 'that is music to my ears.'"

I took off Pete's Brewers hat and tossed it onto the ground and ran ahead. He groaned and cradled a cracked rib when he picked it back up. When I looked back and saw him holding his side while picking up his hat, I felt bad for a moment. But then I realized he would have done it to me and got over my soft spot.

After the movie was out, a couple of older kids met for a fight behind the Cosmo theatre. The manager of the movie theatre was a short, balding man who noticed the group of boys gathering and walked over to them.

The middle-aged, balding guy with a pot belly took a homemade pair of nunchucks from one of the kids and shook them in his face as he said, "Every time you kids see a movie, you all think you are tough guys. Now get out of here."

The crowd dispersed. We walked back down the quiet streets of our little town as the late summer sun set. The movie had an impact on us. We walked in silence, relishing in the influence of a mighty hero that we needed so desperately.

There was humility in Chuck Norris that we recognized on screen. These character actors provided an example to us. They had their own code and they lived by it. They stood up to evil at any cost. Though the opponent was mightier, good could prevail, if he believed in what he stood for.

I was thinking something like that when Pete pushed me into a parking meter and ran ahead in his limping gait.

* * *

After dinner that night, I got onto my bike and rode around town looking for Dad. A low cloud cover echoed with distant thunder. After I noticed it, a sharp wind blew from the north, dropping the temperature to 65 degrees. There were more birds then, and they flew low in the atmospheric energy. A squad of black-winged grackles flanked me as I pulled out of the drive way.

Now that Dad had a bike, he was ranging more around town but the favorite places were the same—one of the parks, the cemetery, the library, or Dairy Queen for a barbecue.

I crossed the bridge across the Wisconsin River and took the trail that went to Riverside Park. The tree canopy made it darker in an instant and a fog was settling over the river. T.B. Scott Mansion loomed above me, the windows like eyes. I wondered if the ghosts of all the people who died mysteriously on these very grounds were near. Like the man who left the door of the mansion to go see the fireworks on the 4th of July and was never found. Or the woman who went for a walk to inspect the grounds and was never seen again.

Or the rich guy who moved in and went insane shortly after. He died horribly in a torturous asylum in the late 1800's.

The cursed hill of the mansion rises sharply, cut with glacier precision. It's a wall on the right of the trail. I tore down it splitting the fog with my bike.

I pictured one-armed Popcorn Dan waving at me through the fog. The caretaker of Scott Mansion, he went home to visit England and booked himself passage home on the Titanic.

The mossy trail dropped down to run alongside the river and my vision reduced in the mist, so I had to slow down. I entered into the alternate universe that was Riverside Park.

A creepy "being watched" feeling persisted. My bike kept going. The smell of peat moss and ozone filled my senses.

A lightning bolt lit up the sky and the thunder clapped soon after; the storm was here. When I broke out of the trail and entered the back of the park, I saw Dad moving his bicycle into a position under the roof of the open park shelter.

The grills stood up on big posts in the ground like park gargoyles. Dad moved his bike under the roof, leaned it on a picnic table, then started looking for something in the backpack.

"Hi, Dad."

He jumped, then smiled at me. The rain came down hard on the roof. I had just made it before being soaked.

"That was close," he said with a smile. His smile—genuine, tranquil, and slow—indicated he was in a forum of internal reflection. The north wind dropped the temperature a bit more and Dad handed me a sweatshirt with holes in it to put on. We watched the huge raindrops bounce off the blacktop parking lot while the darkened sky lit up with bolts of white lighting.

The moisture in the air seemed to penetrate my clothing and I shivered in the sweatshirt.

"My dad was disappointed in me when I left the seminary. Then he was really mad at me when I got thrown out of Notre Dame. They called them both, Mom and Dad, to come down to the Dean's office. My dad was crying afterward. It was the only time I had seen him cry," Dad noted and lit up a long Marlboro cigarette. "And he was a medic in World War I. Can you imagine the stuff he had seen?"

"Why did he cry?"

Dad didn't answer right away but thought for a while, exhaling smoke. He inhaled so deeply that it took several breaths of exhaling before clear air came out.

"I think it's because he saw in me, what I am right now, today. It was about that time that I had a revelation. I looked at my life, and what was in store for me, and I knew I just couldn't handle it."

"What do you mean you couldn't handle it?"

"Just what I said. I don't really know how to describe it. I had an idea of what life was going to be like and what it required from me, and when I looked in myself, I saw a deficiency. I just knew it was going to be really hard and I might not be able to handle it. I think my dad saw it that day."

Lightning crashed again and the flash showed the river rolling by with a mist riding above the dark water. I imagined a ferryman arriving, pushing a flat boat to the boat landing, then reaching out a long bony finger to beckon us aboard.

"I suppose he would not be proud of me to see me in the condition I am in. I'm a failure with nothing to my name—no house, no car, no job, and no real means to get any of it." Then he got up and took his bedroll off his bike, like the Trek might have been a horse in a cowboy movie.

"I sure miss my dad, especially when things are hard, like they are now, like they have been for years. I suppose when you feel alone, you always miss most the people who were closest to you."

"I'm here," I replied.

"And I'm glad of that, old buddy. You are my buddy, and it makes me very happy to be able to spend time with you. I can't stay here much longer. When the summer ends, I have to go away. It will be too cold to sleep outside here. We bums need to think about a warmer climate to survive in. Otherwise, you wake up dead."

"Wake up dead?"

"Yeah, you wake up looking like this." Dad made a grimace and stuck his hands out like they were in a death grip. The goofy face he made got me laughing.

"Where will you go?"

In the pockets of the sweatshirt he had handed me, my hand found a book of matches from The Road House in Tomahawk and a compass. I opened the lid of the compass and looked through the sight wire and took a reading of mils and degrees.

"Last winter, I lived in San Clemente, California, in a campground called San Onofre. I lived right on the beach. That's where the campsites are—right on the beach—and they are affordable, like seven-dollars-a-day, so I have to find a way to earn some money before I go." He rolled out his bedroll on the picnic table and set his glasses beside the wool army blanket.

Then he fidgeted in his backpack, found a flashlight, and tried it out. He aimed it around the park.

"Richard Putnam owes me three hundred dollars and says he will pay me when he sells a house in a few weeks. He gets a commission check then." Dad took his shoes off and swung his legs up onto the table and stretched out on top of it. He lay down like it was a king-sized bed of satin sheets.

He was putting together a plan and I watched it affect his mood.

"And this guy from Tomahawk owes me four hundred for handling his bankruptcy. If I get that, I should have enough to get out of town and live down there for a while. If I don't spend it all, I should have enough to hang out there on minimal provisions, if I live tight, and nothing goes wrong, and I don't get sick." Then he smiled.

"What?"

"I was just cracking up. Never thought I'd end up this way, living in a park, telling my kid how I am going to be a bum for the winter and hopefully survive the experience. Don't end up like this, kid. Keep yourself close to God and obey his commandments so that you may not incur his wrath."

"What do you do out there, on the beach all day?"

"There is a little community of people that live in the park. I know some of them and help them with legal problems. There is a nice couple that lives in a motor home that stays all winter in the park. They invite me in for dinner once in a while. There are surfers that smoke dope, hanging out on the beach during the day and, at night, they have big parties on the beach and drink wapatui."

"Whapa what?"

"They pour a bunch of booze in a bucket and serve it out in cups and get drunk. For the most part, it is a nice community and the people are kind. But of course you have the transient population of criminals roaming all over southern California. It is the land of the whacko.

"I spend my days on the beach, soaking up rays and reading books. There is a bus I take into town to get ice every other day and food supplies. If I need money bad, there is a car wash in town owned by this guy from Red China. He runs the business like a tyrant and has everyone running around working, but he pays cash at the end of the day. I can earn some money there."

"That sounds kind of fun."

"Yes, I guess it does, but all I think about is your mother and you guys. The surroundings are nice but I am lonely everywhere I go. No matter where you go, there you are. But it is beautiful. I don't mean to say it is not. I have slept in open rail cars and woken up to see a Kansas sunrise that stopped my breath—it was so pretty. A glowing lightshow of red and pink appeared on the horizon, and I forgot my agony for a minute. I have slept on a rooftop in San Francisco and basked in a sunset that no one could ever paint.

"I met Diane Keaton in a restaurant, and she flirted with me."

"Really?" I tried to think of who that was.

"Well, she talked to me. Sometimes it's hard for a man to know if a woman is just being nice or if she is flirting. I prefer to see it my way." Dad cinched up his saddle bags on his bike and looked at the chain.

"Sure. Then after I left the restaurant, I got on a bus and I sat next to this lady who didn't have any food or money to feed her three kids. Her husband had just left them. She wanted a man to help her, but when she found out I was basically in the same state of dysfunction as she was, she moved on. And wisely so. But that poor lady was so desperate. One of the worst things about having nothing is that you can offer no real help to those around you, and that's what we're called to do."

The storm dropped down plumes of water around us, and the evening moisture seeped in and dampened everything I touched.

"I am not proud to tell you that I have eaten meals out of a dumpster from hunger. Once I become desperate in circumstance, I can quickly recognize other people who are in a similar situation. I have a strong understanding of what the poor go through in America, and it sucks."

We watched the storm move through the park and talked of dreams, like buying a winning lottery ticket. We talked about what we would do with the money and where we would go. But neither of us had any way to make them happen. They were just dreams. But in the rainy air, they tasted just as sweet to us.

From the fringe of society, we filled the void of the forlorn on the outskirts of the city with imaginary visualizations that I had already learned to adore. And, from here in the haunted park, we painted a different world, even if we could breathe no life into it. We dreamed and waited for the rain to pass.

CHAPTER 18

A stand against many opponents is when an individual fights against a group. Drawing both long and short swords, you hold them out to the left and the right, extending. The idea is that even if opponents come at you from all four sides, you chase them into one place.

The Book of Five Rings, Miyamoto Musashi

Sit down before fact as a little child.

Thomas Henry Huxley

The summer was parading past, the days were bright and long, and the glare off the pool water couldn't dull the image of Trish in her swimsuit. She was confident and seemed to attack the lesson, making me feel like a wimp for shivering in the 7 a.m. class.

I leaned on the fence while watching the lifeguards, who were high school girls, blow their whistles and boss the kids around, remembering my two weeks earlier in the summer. I was grateful that my time was done. Mom was already talking about signing me up for another lesson before the end of the summer and, as I watched through the wire fence, the image of a concentration camp came to mind. It would be colder later in the summer.

When the class ended, Trish came out of the exit with her wet hair pulled back. The slight, olive hue of her skin shone in the direct sunlight and offset the beauty of her eyes. We stepped away from the burning aroma of chlorine into a slight breeze of lilacs until her lavender swirled around me.

We chatted of little things that we might have in common. She seemed distracted and I gave her room in the silence.

"I might be moving far away from here," Trish said from some hollow place within her. I didn't say anything but kept the slow pace she had set in our walk. "My aunt lives in Louisiana, just outside of New Orleans. I think I am going to live with her for a while."

"Why? Don't you like it here?"

"I do like it here, and I love the north woods, but my dad started drinking again and, when he drinks, he is such an asshole." She was flushed with emotion and her eyes flared and narrowed. I let some steps pass. The swear word just didn't sound right coming out of her mouth.

"They have alligators and oysters down there," I remarked. She kept looking down at the ground. "And voodoo dolls and zombies." That got a smile out of her.

"My aunt knows a practicing voodoo priestess and she claims that she saw a zombie—a walking dead person—who had been given that terrible drug that fries their brain out. When initially administered, it can simulate death, and people were buried alive from it, and actually clawed their way out of graves."

"Yeah, and they walk around like this," I said and did my best zombie imitation—walking with stiff limbs in jerky motion and my mouth hanging open. "More brain…more brains," I said in zombie dialect.

I pictured zombies coming out of the ground in an old-time, civil war era. I saw Confederate zombies dragging a leg and hurriedly running down people. They were eating their brains, some standing over the dead like a lion over a fresh kill. I imagined women in big, fancy dresses of the era with noses and ears rotted off, moving toward me in a false love embrace, just to get near me so they could bite my head open.

"Hey, did you hear me?" Trish said. "I asked if you have ever been there."

"No, um, no, I haven't."

"Where do you go, when you slip away like that?" she asked, smiling at me.

"I don't go anywhere. I'm…writing."

Of course, Cajun—that was the exotic beauty I had been seeing in her. I thought of the bullets in the wall of the living room of Richard's house, and the matching casings.

"Maybe this will work out where you can stay here in Merrill," I offered.

She pulled her arms around her shoulders and didn't answer me. Her wet hair dripped down the back of her shirt.

I put my arm around her, resting it gently over her frame and pulled her to my shoulder. She was shuddering when I touched her. She tensed but didn't object. Trying to stay in pace was a little awkward, but I liked the feel of her slender shoulder touching mine.

When we walked up to her house, the yellow pickup was in the driveway, and she stepped away from me. I put my arm at my side. The screen door flew open and her dad walked out with a beer can in his hand and a cigarette in his lips. He caught the door on the backswing as he stepped out. His right hand took the cigarette and he dragged on it, looking at me hard. The amber glow from the cigarette tip was as fierce as his eyes.

I kept pace beside Trish and approached him, meeting his eyes. His lids narrowed just a bit. I glanced away at a dog, a Border Collie I think, that approached us with his tail wagging and head down. I scratched his ears.

"Hey, boy, you the welcome committee?" I said, petting the thick fur. When I looked up, Derrick Lawson was still glaring at me.

"Daddy, this is my friend, Jamie."

"Nice to meet you," I said.

"I know you from someplace," Derrick replied.

"Jamie walked me home from swimming lessons."

"I've seen you before. What is your last name?" He turned his head sideways and exhaled a plume of white smoke that moved toward me in the breeze like a chemical weapon attack.

"Finucan."

"Oh yeah, your dad a lawyer?"

"Yes."

"He helped out a buddy a mine who got busted for drunk driving. Got him off, in fact. I heard he got shot at a few weeks ago."

"Yeah."

I looked down at the friendly dog and back at Derrick.

"He is lucky to be alive. Know what that tells me?" He stepped down off the porch and started walking toward me.

"A coward can't control his fire?" I snapped back. He moved up close to look at me. I suspected he was putting it together now, that he had watched me at Richard Putnam's farmhouse, trailing his foot prints out to the road.

"No, it means your Dad is hanging out with the wrong people," he countered. "I know where I seen you. At the Dairy Queen when that fucking dog scratched my truck. Do you know whose fucking dog that was?"

"No," I lied and shook my head in mock sorrow and regret. Gus would get an extra bacon snack when I got home.

He turned away from me.

"You were supposed to put the laundry away so I have some socks for the rest of the week," he said to Trish.

"I'll do it," she answered quickly, not wanting this to turn into an embarrassing scene. I could feel the tension coming off her.

"I better go. You got a lesson tomorrow?" I asked.

"No, Tuesday and Thursday." She hesitated, looked at her dad, then moved over to me and kissed me on the cheek. I flushed in exhilaration and looked at Derrick.

"See you then," I responded. "Nice to meet you," I called to her dad. He just stared at me and dragged on his Marlboro.

I walked home as storm clouds gathered in the early afternoon. Low, billowy, cumulonimbus clouds moved in, putting electricity in the air, while distant thunder rolled. The sky took on a yellow quality and the humidity spiked. The energy in the air stood up the hair on my arms and I found myself reveling in the pre-storm prelude. The tempest of energy matched a vortex in me that seemed to carry my feet off the pavement.

That night I dreamed of images of beautiful Cajun girls, zombies, and the cold stare of a shooter looking at me first, eye-to-eye, then through a front sight. I turned to run toward a closing door with heavy legs and the distinctive crack of .22 rifle-fire erupted behind me.

* * *

I was waiting for Trish after her next swimming lesson. She was giving the summer a sweet taste.

I wanted to keep walking with her—the conversation was soothingly comfortable and I liked the way her eyes squinted with laughter when I reached for a joke.

"Let's go to Blue Boats. We can go swimming there," I suggested, walking toward the pines behind my mom and step-dad's house. We walked past the spot where the boxing ring had been set up for Shawn's fight. It was okay that she didn't know anything about it. She was dialed into a different frequency.

The trail through the woods was sandy in some spots, covered in a thick blanket of sweet-smelling pine in others. I almost took her hand to lead the way, but some insecurity stopped me.

We rounded the corner and she looked at the massive tree with the rope swing dangling over the water.

"This is the Prairie River. They have a dam over there that creates energy. The dam makes this little swimming hole."

I ran at the tree, jumped off the massive root structure that also worked as our climbing ladder and caught the end of the rope in mid-air. I let my inertia gather in the arc of a swing, but didn't drop into the water. I rode it back to the root and handed it to Trish.

She took it playfully and moved to swing out over the water.

"Stop," I shouted. I looked around, for the first time, missing the park bench. "Just a sec." I jumped off the root, swam out to the distance of the rope apex in swing, and dove down under the cool water. The bench was braced upright beneath the surface, waiting for a victim. I pulled it out and dragged it back onto land.

Trish handed me the wooden rope swing handle, perplexed.

"Some asshole has been trying to kill me by putting this out there where I land on it when I let go."

"Oh, no." She looked at me like I had saved her life. I smiled.

"I landed on it already this summer and damn near drown out there with a fractured spine."

"Who would want to do such a thing?"

"There are a lot of nut jobs out there. My dad just got shot at by some lunatic," I replied, watching her. She didn't respond.

The day was hot and bright. We swam out in the lake to the middle.

"Is that the dam right there?" Trish asked.

"Yeah, it sounds like a flood gate is open right now."

"Are we in any danger?"

"I don't think so. The water draws through the bottom of the flood gates, so it loads from the bottom. The dam down by the Cosmo loads water from the top, so it's easy to be sucked into it and then go through it."

"People get pulled through the dam?"

"Yeah, some survive, but not many. Every few years someone goes through the dam downtown." We were talking heads on a lake of blue water. The sun played off her wet head and complexion, making her exotically beautiful.

I imagined us getting married and me having an argument with her on a Saturday morning in front of Zettler's Bakery about the stuff we owned together.

We talked about school, kids we knew, subjects of study, ambitions of what we wanted to be, and when we got out of the water and stood drying off, we talked of dreams.

"I want to be a doctor," Trish declared, "travel the world, and help people who would otherwise not get medical help. There is a group called Doctors Without Borders. They go into every dark corner of the earth and bring medical expertise to poor people. I think about that. What about you?"

"It's not as noble as yours. I want to write screenplays, maybe even direct movies." It didn't sound so crazy when I said it to her.

We got hungry at lunch time. I didn't want our date to end.

"You should see this. Follow me." I led her down one of the many rabbit trails from the beach into the woods. We came to the snare that Pete and I had set the day before and there was a rabbit caught in the wire. It had struggled against the wire garrote around its neck and expired some time ago. Now, no longer warm to the touch, it was stiff.

"Awww," she said in sympathy and a little shock.

"It's okay. Think of the forest as a farm. Animals die out here." I took the limp rabbit out of the trap. The fleas had all jumped off within the first few minutes of the body temperature dropping. We walked back to the beach area with the dead rabbit. I picked up sticks along the way that were dry and dead.

"My uncle Mike showed me this way of gutting a rabbit." I took the rabbit by the head and swung it around in a large windmill circle, hard, for eight revolutions. I stopped and held it up; all the guts had been gathered by the inertia of the movement into a wad at the bottom of the rabbit's stomach. I showed it to her, with a David Copperfield hand presentation.

With my Barlow jack knife that Bob had given me, I made a small incision in the bottom of the gut bulge. Then I started swinging the rabbit around hard again, in a big circle, alongside myself.

"What are you doing?" Trish asked with a half a smile and half a grimace of grossness on her gorgeous face.

"Watch." At about the seventh swing, I felt the rabbit get lighter. I stopped and held up the rabbit; the stomach was now shriveled up, the guts gone. I looked around slowly, I felt my neck tuck into my shoulders and I hoped for the best.

The glob of rabbit guts plopped down just inches from Trish. The entrails and innards smacked down on the grass next to her and she jumped, pulling her arms to herself and screamed.

"It's okay. It missed you. That's the only problem with that method of gutting the rabbit. You never know where the entrails will land."

I wondered if this was such a good idea.

"What the hell?" she said, stunned. What a mood buster. I got the fire lit fast and pulled the hide off the small dead animal.

"This fur makes a good nightstand cover. My brother, Shawn, tanned the hide of a rabbit and it looks nice under his clock radio," I noted, holding up the hide. She tried to conceal a smile, confusing me slightly.

I cooked the rabbit on the little fire after I quartered it up with my jack knife. We held the greasy bones in our fingers and gnawed the soft, dark meat.

"This is very good," she exclaimed. I think she was surprised to find the game so delicious.

"Hunger is the best seasoning," I replied.

After we ate, we sat on the grass and talked quietly and confidentially. In our delicious isolation, we confided in each other. She was trying to tell me something and suddenly looked away to catch tears that started falling from her eyes.

"I was raped by my uncle," she confided. Her tone was like she was trying to explain something to me. Silence splashed on us like a bucket of cold water from an evil clown. I didn't know what to say. So I said nothing for a few minutes. She sniffled.

"What kind of scumbag does that?" I wanted to 'Chuck Norris punch' every worthless man in her family. She stood up, wiping her face with her open fingers, expertly catching her running tears while in motion. She was skilled at composing herself.

"I have to go home. It's going to rain and we should get going." She didn't look at me as she spoke. We walked back the trail in silence. I was confused and mad at myself for not knowing how to handle this new information, or what to say.

When she figured out the way through the woods, she stepped a little faster than me and walked in front of me. I stayed with her until she got to her block. Then she turned and forced a smile at me.

"You don't have to come any closer to my house. My dad is home and he embarrasses me if he is drinking. And now he's always drinking."

"I had fun with you today," I answered.

Trish stopped for a second, then turned back toward me. She kissed my mouth.

"You're so sweet," she added with an electric spark in her dark eye. I watched her go into the dysfunctional home, feeling like a bag of bones standing in wet clothes.

Rain fell on the walk home, but I hardly noticed. Her kiss still felt warm on my mouth. My imagination played with Trish Lawton. I wanted to learn to play the piano so I could play a song and impress her. I wished I could drive a car, because I wanted to pick her up for a ride in a Chevy Nova. I wanted to learn to fly so I could pilot us to a small island and enjoy a weekend playing chicken fights in the water with people from all over the world.

The vanilla taste filled my senses and the sunlight changed things to a different yellow lighting. The Olympic Russian Karate team was making their way toward me at Normal Park, jogging at me in anticipation, their white gi's contrasting their black belts. The barefoot assassins closed the distance. I waved them off; I didn't have time for such nonsense. I wasn't a kid anymore—I was kissing girls.

With Trish drifting around in my brain like a cool mint mist, I ran for home. I stayed off the sidewalks and moved through the backyards, watching for dogs, jumping fences, and ducking clotheslines. This way, I moved through town without being seen. I was behind enemy lines, in war-torn Europe, moving toward the border.

On my bike the next day, I found Dad sleeping in Normal Park again. The shapes of houses and cars were becoming visible in the early morning light. I sat down this time, and didn't wake him. Instead, I watched the morning light grow and show me the summer day that lay out around me.

After a while he must have sensed my presence. He woke up as though he had been sleeping light. He saw me sitting on the grass and his eyes knew I was there with bad news.

"What is it?" he asked. His eyes fluttered in the morning light. He looked around like he didn't know where he was or why he was outside.

"Gertie died last night." The stroke at the beginning of the summer had taken a few months to claim her.

Dad pulled his knees up and peered around. He looked like he had the panic feeling of loneliness coming upon him. He gazed around him for some kind of landmark perhaps. We sat together in silence for minutes.

"I should have gone to see her," he said and wept. The tears came from the pit of his soul.

I leaned my head on my handle bars and tried to watch the cars go by on Center Avenue. As I looked at them whizzing by, the faces stared at us. I wasn't ashamed anymore. I felt the rage light and flipped up my middle finger at the faces in an Oldsmobile. They stared back in horror.

More time passed. Dad was now pulling himself tighter and I didn't know what to say. He sensed it and glanced at me.

"Thanks, Jamie. You can run along now."

I rolled away on my bike feeling like I had lost something.

Chapter 19

In the happiest of your childhood memories, our parents were happy, too.
Robert Brault

In distinguishing the advantages of the tools of warriors, we find that whatever the weapon, there is a time and situation in which it is appropriate.
The Book of Five Rings, Miyamoto Musashi

"Well," said I, "I've come aboard to take possession of this ship, Mr. Hands; and you'll please regard me as your captain until further notice."
Treasure Island, Robert Louis Stevenson

The T.B. Scott library was donated by the Scott family after Mr. Scott's death. Besides being a fantastic legacy to leave the community, it was a place of refuge in the summer when it rained.

Here I could forget that one of the 90 days of summer bliss was closed to outdoor activities because of the weather. I could spend hours browsing, exploring, and tunneling from one subject to another with impromptu research.

Afternoons could dissolve quickly into the delight of fascination and discovery. I read about the American Indian uprising of 1862, and then trailed off to a book on how to survive in the outdoors. I might see a book on crime detection and get lost in that for a while, and then see a book spine on ocean exploration, pick that up, and sit down at one of the tables with it.

In this place, my imagination was not such a dragon to contain; I could let it out and feed it. The enforced silence was right and sane to me. This place of contemplation and study signaled to me some solemn normality.

The aisles of books smelled of musty knowledge. I had escaped the boredom of a rainy day by staying busy. I had taken my notebook and a book I found to a table that had a sunbeam working its way across the oak surface.

I had intended to complete the detective story I was writing, but got side-tracked when I found a book on the exploration of the Antarctic and a guy named Shackleton. The adventure was turning out to be a disastrous voyage. The ship was frozen in the ocean and the crew was abandoning the vessel on the ice when a pair of hands closed over my eyes from behind and I felt a weight against the back of my head.

I froze. If Krumel had found me, his steel-toed boots would make contact, not soft hands. The touch was too gentle to be an enemy. In confusion I froze, until I smelled the lavender and knew who it was.

Trish Lawton stepped around beside me, showing me a big smile. I exhaled in relief.

"Did I scare you?"

"I thought you were someone else. I was wrong. Sorry," I replied in release, switching modes.

"Who else would come up on you like that?"

"Oh, you'd be surprised."

We chatted in a hushed tone under the watchful eye of the librarian who was much more lenient in the summer. Trish's foot brushed against mine under the table when she giggled. She laughed so hard at one of my stupid stories that we got the look that was given to the disruptive.

"What's this?" Trish asked and slid my blue-covered notebook over the table to herself. My hand slapped down on it too fast, pinning it to the table.

"Nothing."

She looked at me with a silent accusation of withholding myself. Her eyes melted the part of me that hides my writing.

"I thought we share things," she said. She couldn't know what she was asking. No one ever read this stuff. I still hesitated. Why didn't she just ask me to stab a short Samurai sword into my own belly? That might have been easier.

"You can't read my handwriting." I thought that was a safe bet.

"Let me try."

The fact that I was hiding the contents of the notebook seemed to harden her resolve. I didn't know a lot about Cajun women, but I saw now that if they wanted something, they knew how to go about getting it. Both of our hands were pressed down on the notebook and we faced each other across the table.

"I don't think that's a good idea." I was sweating and not knowing why. She tilted her head just a bit and parted her bee-stung lips.

I slowly eased up the downward pressure in my hand, like a reverse board break in karate. No one had ever read from one of these notebooks. Trish slid it away from me and proceeded to open it like she was spinning the combinations of a lock.

She pushed the long, black hair on the right side of her head back behind her ear, so it wouldn't hang over the paper, and began reading.

I fidgeted, then put my attention to the Shackleton story again, but reread the same paragraph over and over. She laughed at first.

"This Gross Joe thing is so funny."

She held up her dark hand over her face, glancing at me to see if I was offended at her laughing at me.

I was bothered by something. My subconscious mind was setting off an internal alarm about the content of the notebook and a feeling of regret was welling up in me. I tried to think of what I had written to fill those pages.

Her expression changed as she read on. She leaned over it and her concentration factor went up. At one point she held a hand over her mouth in exasperation, or horror; I couldn't be sure. When at last she finished, she shut the blue notebook and it seemed to slam with a bang.

"The whole detective thing—you were asking me those questions. You were asking me about my dad, just trying to find out who was shooting at your dad. Is that what you were doing? Pretending to be my friend so you could get in my house and look for a gun?"

I froze again. What the hell had I written in that notebook?

"You were investigating my dad. That's why you came over and talked to me. That's why you picked up the gun in our house. That's why you have been walking me home from swimming class."

The part of her natural expression of vulnerability now showed itself in anguish. It broke my heart and made me feel like a jerk.

"It started like that Trish, but I think we got to be good friends." Nothing else came from the well of knowing what to say.

"Well, did you get what you wanted, Gross Joe?" She spun my notebook across the table at me. Her look could have extinguished a candle.

"Well, you tell me. Your dad shoots off ten rounds through a window at my dad. Don't tell me you didn't know anything about it. He chases anything down with that rifle that crosses the yard. The guy has some issues. Someone's going to get hurt if nothing is done," I said too loudly.

She shot up from her seat and looked around the table for a moment.

"So that was you running off through the yard." Her tone sounded unnatural.

"Sit down, come on, and don't run off." As I stood up with her, I tried to bring my voice down.

"No. You know what, Jamie Finucan?" She was composing herself for her exit. "I thought you were someone else. I was wrong. Now, I'm sorry." She stepped with fury and spun away.

I sat there with the book on Shackleton and the notebook in front of me. It would be a long time before anyone read anything I wrote again.

I could identify with Shackleton as he stood on the ice with his few possessions around him on the bright, white, cold berg.

* * *

In my notebook I wrote:

Bring swimming suit home from Purcell's house.

Gross Joe has enough.

Gross Joe was coming home after a long day to his one-bedroom flop with the community bathroom down the hall.

He was walking across the parking lot when the two men appeared. They stepped out together from the shadows.

"Did you two freaks kick any puppies on the way over here?" Joe taunted and coughed a few times. He needed to charge up his natural weapon.

Bald Man moved in with a punch. Joe ducked it and gobbed a thick wad of phlegm from the back of his throat at Nunchucker. It felt like a quarter-pound of mass leaving his lungs.

The glob flew straight into the man's eyes.

Joe ducked the second punch from Bald Man and kicked Nunchucker in the balls, hard. Nunchucker went down to one knee, then the other. Then he clattered to the ground.

"Every time you rejects with no identity see a Chuck Norris movie, you think you are kick-boxing champions. But you are just a couple of assholes. And you, trying to be like Chuck Norris—you aren't a pimple on the ass of Chuck. Let me tell you something: when it's time to die, the Grim Reaper shows up. When it's time for the Grim Reaper to die, Chuck Norris shows up."

The big bald guy with the messed-up ears even cracked up, between his groans.

That encouraged Joe.

"And I will tell you something else: when Chuck Norris crosses the street, the cars look both ways."

Bald Man cracked up and tried to get up.

"Shut up," the Chuck wannabe said.

"Let me tell you something, you punk," Joe replied while stretching out some tendons that were bruised in his shoulder. "When you were a kid, you played 'kick the can.' Well, as a kid, Chuck Norris liked to play 'kick the kid.'"

"Screw you," Chuck Wannabe said pulling himself up to his knees.

"Trying to wear your hair like Chuck. Listen, you 'never was,' Chuck Norris actually has a diary. It's called the *Guinness Book of World Records.*"

Now even Nunchuker was smiling. Bald Man was squirting out laughter, stopping only to prevent from choking on his own blood until he could roll over.

Even Joe was laughing.

"Listen, as a kid, Chuck Norris sent his dad to his room."

"Enough," pleaded Nunchucker. "No shit, Joe, you just kicked our asses, don't kill us with jokes."

"Chuck Norris puts the laughter in manslaughter…" Joe couldn't get it all the way out and had to start the joke twice, before he could deliver it effectively, so that the two guys on the pavement could hear it. But they were laughing already, watching Joe trying to tell the joke. The three men were almost incapacitated from hilarity.

"Let me tell you something, Chuck Norris can kill your imaginary friends." The power of shared laughter bonded them.

"Hey, you guys are alright. Come on, there is a pizza parlor down the street. You can buy me a pizza and a beer, and I will act like I like you two ass wads. And maybe I won't kick your ass again." They all laughed.

Then Joe stopped and looked at them hard. They got nervous and then they all started laughing again.

All three walked down the street to Carlo's Pizza. Joe actually preferred the rigatoni there and let the two goons eat an entire large, hand-tossed, pepperoni, sausage and pineapple, like it was nothing.

Joe tried to teach them the art of the Chuck Norris joke, but they could not create, only destroy. When the food hit the table, none of it had a chance. For they were big, hungry men.

* * *

Dad and I stepped out of church just before the priest left the altar so we wouldn't have to interact with the congregation. When the priest had petitioned for prayers, Dad had made one of his outcries of injustice.

"That the community of Merrill changes its flaky attitude toward the poor and that this parish recognizes them as humans who should be treated with dignity, we pray to the Lord." Dad's words dripped with accusation.

The people looked our way. A moment of silence ensued. Then the priest said:

"And for this, we pray to the Lord." A few people even said it with him.

Dad saw himself as the spokesperson for the poor. Some of the nuns saw him as a prophet that was sent by God to point out inequality. I was horrified each time he did it. It seemed self-righteous to take such a position—the spokesperson of the poor.

We walked out of the church and down the steps.

"Did you hear that song leader? Someone should have thrown something at her," he ridiculed.

I resented the outburst. Today it was all not sitting well with me.

Dad carried his missal in his hand and walked with a slight limp today, as though he had a stiff knee.

"These assholes call themselves Christians, tell themselves they're helping people, and all they really look after is their own ass. None of them knows what it's like to be poor, or could handle a simple minute of it if they had to. They lock this church at night. Tell me how can you do that? This is God's house. It is supposed to be open to everyone. If I try to sleep in here on a cold night, they throw me out like a vagrant."

He didn't have his bike with him so I walked mine beside him. The cars that left the church stared at us with wrinkled old faces.

At Chip's Hamburgers, we sat at the outdoor picnic tables with circular chairs painted bright colors that made me think of riding a balloon.

One of the restaurant's stockholders was a Green Bay Packer named Ray Nitschke. Every once in a while, Ray showed up in Merrill and signed autographs for fans. In a matter of minutes, a line formed around the block to meet him.

Dad's mood was dark and I didn't want it to get into my head.

I bit into a Blue Jay burger and wished Ray Nitschke was here now so I could meet him. Instead, Dad was droning on about the poor and how shitty it was to be broke and have no one care.

I imagined what the small restaurant looked like when Ray Nitschke was here, perhaps sitting at this very table. Kids lined up around the block just to glimpse the legend. He sat at the table. It tipped slightly with his weight. He wore the jersey with 66 on it and smiled that million-dollar, professional-athlete smile of the truly-elite gladiators of the planet.

"You know your dad is just venting. He has had a hard time of it," Ray might have said to me as he signed an autograph for Jenny Wilson. Jenny would look at me with amazement, sitting next to Ray Nitschke, and him talking to me like I was a buddy.

I would look away, like I hardly noticed her.

"I know, Ray. You came from a tough background, what with your parents dying when you were young. You overcame anything in your way. You never had an excuse. You didn't whine about how tough life was. When a man makes a mistake, he earns the consequences. Hell, Ray, I'm eleven and I understand that."

"Hey, you should have more respect for your father. He isn't feeling well." Ray stood up. "You're doing okay, kid. You're a trooper for sticking by him in a tough time. That will be remembered and will serve you well. Your friendship with your father will serve to give you comfort later in life."

My vision faded with Ray Nitschke turning to leave and slamming hard into Erik Krumel, who went flying and landed on his back on the pavement.

Everyone in line applauded.

"Hey, kid, can you hear me or did you trip out to la-la land?" Dad was asking me. His annoyance transformed into a concern. I was hurt by his tone.

"I heard you." I wondered if every kid my age thought he was a freak.

"I was saying, I had everything taken from me. My life has had the joy wrung out of it, like a wet pair of jeans." He pantomimed the gestures of wringing out a pair of jeans.

"This town went for me, all of them. They ganged up on me. The lawyers in this town—they turned on me when they saw I wouldn't play their game. One of these pricks turned me in to the state bar for having a hatchet on my stationery. My office was in Tomahawk, which is the symbol of the town. These pricks in this town did everything they could to destroy me."

"Dad, that just doesn't sound right. I met Judge Schnabel and he has respect for you and wishes you well. He told me you were a brilliant lawyer and offered me help if I ever needed it."

"He said that?" Dad asked in surprise.

"Yes. No one ganged up on you. You made some choices. Some say you lost by way of your own hand." I had had enough of the tirade today.

"Each man is the architect of his own future," I insisted, having recalled the statement I had just read in the inside cover of a library book.

"You have a college education and a law degree. You had a better shake at it than most." I put down the Blue Jay burger and grabbed my napkin. The juices were running down my hand. Dad looked at me for a moment, then looked away, deflated.

"If I ever talked to my father that way, he would have slapped my mouth."

"Never slap a man who has a mouthful of food." I was reaching for a smile in the situation—my only way in retreat, anytime I needed to.

"I am not talking disrespectfully," I added. "I am speaking the truth, and you and I have an agreement to do so always. We reap what we sow; it's in the Bible. We earn everything we get and that happens to us. The Hindu's call it Karma or something. You are responsible for your life. If not you, who?" I asked while dipping a French fry in ketchup that I had squirted on the wax paper holding my juicy, greasy burger.

"So you are a ten-year-old kid who has all the answers now?"

"I'm eleven, and any answers I have learned, I learned from you. After all, I have a genius for a dad." I smiled. "Everyone who knows you says that about you."

Dad didn't take the bait or way out. He pushed away his food, looking off to the side to watch the street, so he wouldn't have to look at me. I finished lunch in the sunshine with the cars passing on the street.

CHAPTER 20

Do not take short cuts at the cost of clarity.
The Elements of Style, Strunk and White

Some sins we commit cry out for God's vengeance.
Pat Finucan

From the blue notebook:

Gross Joe was trying to talk some sense into the thick scull of his buddy Frank Guts.

"Now stay with me, Frankie. Remember the story of Tommy 2Guns?" Joe asked him.

"No. Tommy 2Guns—what did they call him that for?" Frank had to ask.

"Because he liked to carry two guns. It gave him a nickname. If the coppers find a body with bullet holes from two different caliber guns, it might be Tommy 2Guns. Tommy likes the street cred—gives him a name, though he's just a two-bit piece of crap."

"Yeah, I follow you. Tommy 2Guns. I like it," Frank said, nodding like a Pez dispenser.

"So guess what. He gets tired of carrying around two guns. They're heavy. Two guns is two pains in the ass. Know what I mean?" Joe said.

"Hey, you don't have to tell me," Frank Guts replied, nodding like a bobble head.

"So what do you think he does about it?" Joe asked.

"He carried around only one gun—shed one of those pieces of heat."

Joe slapped him harder than he meant to.

"No, when your name is Tommy 2Guns, you carry two guns. Do you think anyone out there cares if the guns are heavy? When people come for you, they'll come for a well-armed man and you damn sure better not disappoint them," Joe said, looking like a sensei who failed a student.

"Jeeze, Joe, you didn't have to slap me. You don't even wash your hands after you take a crap. I'd appreciate it if you kept your filthy meathooks off me."

Joe belched: "They don't call me Gross Joe for nuthin," in one big burp.

* * *

I was dressed up for Gertie's funeral and saw all my cousins. My cousin Father Tom Finucan came. He was running Viterbo College in La Crosse, and Father Monsieur Jim Finucan was there. I saw Aunt Marcella, who later left me a thousand dollars from her will. My aunt Mary was there with her Irish charm and kindness toward me.

Grandma Gertie was the first dead person I ever saw. Her body lay in the casket but I knew it wasn't her. She was gone, but somehow in death she kept her stoic nature under the waxed work of the mortician. I recalled my visits to her apartment. She smoked, asked me how school was, and offered me a piece of black liquorice candy.

Gertie's life was over now, a widow of a World War I veteran medic. I wondered what Grandpa Jim might have said to her about all the carnage he had seen. Gertie was a master piano player and taught lessons out of her house to the Merrill community. I knew her pickled watermelon rind to be better than candy.

For the first time, I felt the loss of a fallen family member and their slam of the exit door when they leave this world, and I would feel it again through life. I learned at that funeral the terrible finality of death.

After the funeral I noticed the funny silence through the family. Then I realized Dad was not there. He hadn't attended his own mother's funeral.

* * *

Deirdre had returned from visiting our cousins, the Gulotte's, in Florida, with a new attitude. She distanced herself from friends with pot-smoking values, to ones that played sports. She dumped her boyfriend Darrel and became an athlete in school henceforth.

In the middle of the night, I heard Darrel baying like a dog outside the house. She had locked him out of the house and he was calling to her like a lovesick, drunk puppy.

The dream that pulled me from my sleep was one of a hunter tracking a wounded bear that had been arrowed in a hunt. The bear was now doing its death song. I was pulled from sleep as the song turned to human baying outside the window—obvious emotional agony. I looked out the window and, in the front yard, under the moonlight, I saw his tall, long-haired silhouette moaning and calling out my sister's name.

"I broke up with him. Don't let him in," Deirdre said, passing me in the hallway as she went back to her room.

"Cool." I followed her into her room. "Why the change?"

"At the Gulotte's, I saw how they lived. It was very different. The cousins are all out for sports and involved in clubs and church groups. They don't smoke pot or drink, and do really good in school. They seem happier, like they have it together. We laughed a lot without having any drama.

"I am going to do it that way. I have wasted enough time."

I went to the room I shared with Tim. Darrel's serenade of self-pity went on outside the house. We watched Shawn calmly walk out into the street light toward Darrel. Tim and I went out the front door and stood on the porch. The two of them stood face-to-face in the nearby street light. Darrel taller, Shawn close, ready, calm.

"This has gone on long enough. You need to leave," Shawn said. They exchanged words for a minute, but Darrel staggered toward the edge of the yard. We three boys went back into the house. Before I went back to bed, I looked out the window and saw Darrel wrestling with the mailbox. He was twisting it with his body and punching it. He called out names and curses that sounded like a voodoo incantation.

When at last he accomplished a take-down on the mailbox, he straddled it and began punching it. He slammed his bare-knuckled fist against the metal cylinder. I felt pity for the broken man. He twisted, then tore off the little metal flag that could be put up, and threw it aside.

A wave of curses erupted out of him and his hand lifted and fell in the moonlight, slamming down on the cylindrical metal tube.

He was a man filled with the anguish of having lost the best thing in his life.

It was impressive, I had to admit. If someone needed the shit kicked out of a mailbox, this guy could get the job done.

I imagined a gangster saying to his henchmen: "Send him a message." Darrel would show up and fight the mailbox in front of their house. The mark would come out and look at the twisted wreckage.

"Okay, I'll have the money by Friday," the mark would say.

As he went on, it became sadder to all of us who listened and watched. We went from chuckling beside each other, to the smiles sliding off our faces in discomfort.

At the end of it, he wept, cradling his bloody hands against his stomach and leaning down, then lying his head against the downed metal box. He wept bitter tears of rage. The mailbox had won.

That wouldn't work with my gangster play-out on the mailbox message. If the thug started crying like that, I could see the mark saying, 'What the hell kind of message is this?" to his wife.

"Are you talking to yourself again?" Tim asked me, nudging me hard.

"I prefer to think of it as 'writing,'" I replied.

"They are going to take you away one day if you keep fading out like that. Think I want to visit my little brother in the loony bin?

"No," I responded. He tussled my hair.

"All right, get to sleep, 'little paperback writer'," Tim said as he walked into our bedroom. He put on Bachman Turner Overdrive on the 8-track player and "Let it Roll Down the Highway" played until it clicked over half-way through the track, which was how we went to sleep. The 8-track player would run all night.

I lay in bed with a moonbeam on my forehead and folded my hands behind my head. Love was a strange thing I decided. A car passed by on the highway outside my window making a shshshshsh sound as it rolled past.

When I drifted off, I dreamed I had to pick up these little BB's in a short period of time or something bad would happen. I never knew what it was that would happen, but I grabbed these little BB's and tried to put them in a pillow case as fast as I could. There were so many of them. There was no way to get them all in the sack; the room was full of them. After I had been picking them up, I looked at the sack and discovered a hole in it.

I woke up to my alarm going off on a summer day. It was time for a football game at John's house. He lived on the edge of town and it was a long bike ride. We enjoyed playing football all day until our throats were parched.

As I took off on my bike, I saw Bob fixing the mailbox. Bob waved at me like it was normal procedure to have to straighten out a mailbox after it had been wrestled to the ground. His demeanor was always calm and cool. Bob had a great attitude toward any situation.

As I rode past, I saw blood spattered across the metal tubular box. It seemed to have come from the inside of it.

CHAPTER 21

"Of course nothing bad ever happens to a writer. It's all just material for a book one day."
Garrison Keillor

The tempestuous energy of the summer was growing around me in the warm wind. I felt I had solved the crime of attempted murder of my dad. This knowledge was turning in my mind and challenging me to action.

I had the feeling that I needed support in handling this problem. I did what I would do all my life—run to my dad for advice. I found him at the library, browsing in the nonfiction section, looking at a book on Jack the Ripper. Under his suntanned arm he held three books, one on investing, one on "why some people are lucky," and a directory of campgrounds across America.

He stood out in the setting, a hardened, suntanned, middle-aged man with a mop of prematurely gray hair in a mess on his head. His shorts were Patagonia brand. He smelled of coconut suntan oil, which was slathered to a glisten over his arms and shoulders. On his feet were sandals with a single toe strap in the front.

I greeted him and he showed me what he was checking out. He was enthusiastic about learning and reading these topics. Dad immersed himself in subjects of study and discussed them with me for days, analyzing theory on who Jack the Ripper might have been. Or he was reading a book on aggression and was prepared to discuss theory on human behavior. When Dad studied, he experienced a kind of bliss.

"You have to keep your desire for an education alive in spite of the school system," he counseled.

We walked through the quiet building while students wrote in notebooks and old men sat in chairs reading newspapers.

Dad carried his books in a paper bag as we walked across the concrete bridge that led to Stange's Park. We stopped on top of the bridge. The Prairie River tumbled over rocks below us. Dad smoked a cigarette and looked down at the water, feeling something deep for a moment. His eyes told me he was far away, reliving a moment—rolling it around in his mind and weighing it for emotional value or significance.

Books were hard to carry and maintain on his bike. It took tremendous effort to keep them dry, to keep them from getting trashed. Yet he took them everywhere. He usually had one within reach.

The day was overcast, but the temperature was warm at 76 degrees. A wind moved the maple tree tops overhead, and took away the cigarette smoke Dad exhaled like a jet stream.

"I think I know who the guy is who shot at you," I blurted out. "I think he may have thought you were Richard."

His eyes cleared and he turned to face me.

"How do you mean?" Dad asked.

"The guy's name is Derrick Lawton. He works at the paper mill." Dad waited for me to go on. "He has a daughter that is a year older than me in school."

A blue jay made its taunting screech from a treetop behind me.

"Go on."

"John Purcell and I were watching the house and saw a woman that I've seen in Richard's office stop there for a visit. Lawton was real friendly with her. You know what I mean?"

"Yeah."

"I was talking to Trish, his daughter, and went into their house. He keeps the .22 that I think he used to shoot at you behind the door, like he might be expecting trouble."

"You went into his house?"

"Yeah. When I was out at Richard's with you a few weeks ago, I found a .22 casing in the yard, one the sheriff's office missed, by Richard's window." I took out the two, small, brass casings from my pocket.

I extended them both out to him. Dad took a moment to calmly put on his glasses.

"So when I was in Lawton's house, I saw a coffee can with some shells inside of it. A few were empty. I took one. The extractor of his rifle makes a mark on the side of the shell casing. It does it consistently. That was his rifle that fired those shots. So that was him that fired it."

I had to slap a mosquito that was biting the side of my neck, ruining my Colombo act.

"It's the same weapon," I asserted.

"It's the same weapon, but that does not tie him directly to firing it," he said distantly, examining the casings, intense and thoughtful.

Below us, a kid of about seven approached the shoreline, looking into the water. He had a coffee can in one hand and started walking out on the rocks in the water. He stopped to pick up a crayfish and looked at it. Then he put it into his coffee can. The boy focused down as he balanced on the rocks, making his way back to the shoreline, keeping his feet dry.

He was a few years younger than I was, but I found myself envious of his young age. I smelled the vanilla toffee all the time when I was seven. Sometimes I played for days in worlds of imaginary creation, where I fought battles and hunted grizzly bears in the park, or fought Indians who attacked in endless waves. I had dialogues, written impromptu in tirades on victory and defeat, even triumph and shame.

I realized the flavor and smell was coming less with each year of age. I gripped the stone wall of the bridge.

"Why did you follow this dangerous man around and go into his house?" Dad asked.

"I think we need to do something about this."

"You won't do anything about it," Dad asserted. He was looking at the shell casings, his brow furrowed.

"But you said it: nobody is doing anything about this. It's like open season on the Finucans. You are right. Nobody does a damn thing," I said from the rage within.

"You are not going to do anything. This is my fight. You stay out of it. I appreciate your concern, Jamie, but you could get yourself killed. When there is something to be done on this front, as the father, it's my job, and I will do it, if it needs to be done. Promise me right now that you will not take up this matter anymore."

"Why?"

"Good father's do not get their kids in trouble or put them in dangerous situations. I might be homeless and broke, and I might have to put up with shit from everyone all around me, as I am down and out. And I might have to sacrifice huge chunks of my dignity to do things, like eat. And I might have to sleep under this fucking picnic table tonight if it rains, but I am still your father and you will damn well do what I tell you to do. This shooting incident happened to me, not to you. I am the head of this family and this is my fight." His green eyes penetrated to my soul.

"You will stand down immediately from involvement with this."

"So nothing happens?"

"You are to have no more contact with anyone associated with that nut job! Are we clear?" he demanded, looking me in the eye.

"Clear." I was a little more than miffed that my homeless dad had somehow now been able to pull rank as father and was not speaking to me as a buddy anymore. It didn't seem fair that he could jump across the line and play the other side, and now be a big parent. Here he was, acting like a dad.

A boundary line had been marked in our relationship that summer.

We stood there looking at the white water tumbling under the bridge. He was going to go on, remaking the point, making damn sure I understood, rephrasing it, and giving examples, potential outcomes and liabilities. Only I didn't want to hear it. I was unbelievably perturbed by this maneuver. It hurt me for some reason that I didn't understand.

I couldn't identify the feeling or put a thought to it, but something smoldered within me.

"I have to go. I got a bunch of stuff I have to do," I spoke up, and jumped onto my bike. I had left the .22 casings with Dad. I rode away feeling like I had lost much more somehow.

* * *

The summer days were getting shorter and there was never enough time to find a ride out to Eau Claire Dells before it ended. Tom's brothers—two, big, friendly Polish guys who liked to belt out the lyrics of songs on the AM radio—were going out there, so we got a ride.

We even got them to pick up John Purcell on the way.

Eau Claire Dells, or the Dells of the Eau Claire River, is a state park wonder between Merrill and Wausau. It is an enchanting summer place where the river water falls for twelve feet over a cliff, pools up in a ten-by-twelve-foot area, then spills over a second set of rock falls for a two-foot drop.

From the top rock, you can dive off the cliff and plunge down into the water of the Eau Claire River without hitting any rocks—if you stay in the middle of the turbulent pool. After surfacing in the bubbling water, you can slide down the second waterfall through a channel of current that will pull you down at first. If you remain calm, you tumble over the second waterfall. Then you are gently pulled down in the spillway's current, but let back up to the surface in just a few seemingly long seconds.

The swimmer drifts down sheer walls of granite in the black-shadowed water. There is no handhold. Just remain calm and let the water take you, and you flow with the river. Ignore the fingernail scratches in the wet walls from those who lost their cool, who drifted this way before you, for centuries.

Here, swimming in this strong current, I learned a lesson in not fighting the forces that are so much more powerful than you. If you fight yourself in the downward current of the water, you expel your energy trying to swim against thousands of gallons of water, consume your oxygen, and spend yourself in futile struggle. You run out of air quickly, unless you go with the flow.

You can spend all day on the rocks, in the sun, at the park. If you do, the natural water park begins to unveil its secrets to you. Like, if you swim up into the big, mighty waterfall, you can beat it. The current will push you against the slippery rock wall and try to wash you downstream. But if you don't turn your belly to the wall and fight the slippery granite, you could roll into a crawl and make progress.

You had to roll with each stroke, and when you bumped the age-slick wall, you had to keep kicking. And if you held to your stroke, you made headway up the side of the waterfall to be able to slip up next to it, out of the current.

There, it was like a magic portal. Holding yourself tight against the cool, wet rock, the fury of the waterfall thundered past you. The cool mist clings to your skin and the ionic charge hypnotizes you in its magnificence. But there is a rock you can clutch, just below the surface of the water. Grab it and plunge down, but stay close to the wall, and if you can move in another three feet without being torn away by the blasting current, you can find the air pocket.

You come straight up, after traveling in, and there is the tiniest handhold, for just one hand. The other clutches the wet, slippery rock and will never find a place to crook a finger. I know. But by one hand, you can raise your face up out of the torrent and you will be in this air pocket under the waterfall. The sunlight still penetrates the water, and if sunlight ever tumbled, it does there.

The air is incredible, and anyone outside can see something dark, deep in the waterfall. I yell when I'm in there. Everyone does. And the sound of your voice rolls out of the waterfall like the thick, river foam that gathers at the corners of the surface.

You can stay there as long as you like, but you must come out, and that's the hard part. If the park is crowded and people are diving off the rocks into the center tumult, you risk flushing out into someone as they land. And to get out, you must surrender.

You have to let go of the finger hold you have found, like so many Indians so long ago, and surrender to the rolling water at your back. And when you do, it receives you in an instant, and again you are reminded of the power of this river, and the force she wields. She spits you out into the pool, and no one lands on you, so you roll down to the second waterfall, never the same inside.

In the summer, the sun in that park feels like a mother's caress and relieves your pain and worry.

I couldn't wait to get there as we rode out to the Dells of the Eau Claire on twisting country roads, over glacier-carved hills cut into squared, corn-crop fields. We passed old, classic, German-American farm buildings that have housed generations. On the road, tractors travel slowly with orange triangles on their back sides.

We passed a horse and buggy rolling along with a Mennonite man in plain clothes and sideburns, holding fast to the reins of his quarter horses and minding his own. He stared forward as we passed him.

The Dells was a place to escape the heat of the summer. John, Tom, and I were stuffed in the back seat of the Plymouth

Fury. We wore swimming suits, shoes with no socks, and had towels with us. The summer had started and then raced by us, and now there were only a few weeks left. The dreadful specter of going back to school threatened our vacation like a killer storm cloud at a picnic.

When we twisted through the park to get to the swimming area parking lot, I saw the blue AMC Hornet that was known as the Krumel-mobile that his older brother drove.

I got out of the car and grabbed my towel. Maybe Erik didn't come here with his older brother, I hoped, but I knew better.

Everything comes to a head and some conflict has destiny stitched in it. No one in my group noticed the Hornet. I kept it quiet and walked with them down the stone-cut path that led us to the waterfalls. But I let them stride out in front of me. I slowed to think—and look around.

Fear gripped me, I won't lie. I was scared shitless. I reached for the anger and found it not far away from the surface of my mind. I needed it to burn a sense of purpose into my being.

I thought about it all as I followed the group down the granite-carved steps. I breathed deeply, trying to stop the shaking in my legs. I made myself remember the harassing messages through his henchmen, and the beating up of my friends to tell me he was coming for me. It began to piss me off, and I let it.

I clenched my fist and breathed deeply. The time for the main event had arrived. Here, Erik would not have on his steel-toed boots.

The granite walkway led down to a view of the park from high up. Standing before the railing with the park and its smooth stone and waterfalls laid out before me, I saw about twenty-five people lying out on the warm stone, drinking beer and taking time to dip in the turbulent water. Both beautiful and dangerous, those two things have always seemed to go together in my world.

I spotted Krumel with his older brother and four other bigger boys. Their hair was long. A few of them had tattoos.

They were smoking cigarettes and drinking Miller beer in cans. Standing up at the railing, I tried to think of the elements that were in my favor. Krumel was taller, heavier, and had the back-up of family around him. I struggled for a moment, hyperventilating; this would embolden his response.

His force was larger than I could control. Could I use it, rather than fight it?

John and Tom walked down, talking to Tom's brothers, only glancing down at the crowded rocks. I paused at the steel railing and let them walk ahead. A strong sense of dread welled up in me and considered any option other than walking down there.

I remember a moment when I was watching my friends walk away, that I wished they would notice I was not with them, but they were distracted. A surge of loneliness that only the condemned know touched me.

I could run off, straight into the woods, and live on berries and rabbits for a few years. Wait till this all blows over. I smiled at that option. There were no options.

There seemed no element that I could put in my favor. Surprise was not a tool I could use.

I watched the team I had come in with walk past them and settle on the rocks by the water, looking at girls in bikinis. I started walking down.

I needed to keep it in public, where all could see. That was the best chance of having the fight stopped by someone, an authority figure or a bold onlooker, if things didn't go well. But I smiled at the thought. I had been in enough scraps already to know that this rarely happens and onlookers can be counted on to, well, onlook.

Taking the granite-carved steps down to the river, I had a second thought. What if I just went about my business? Would it pass me by? Maybe Mom was right after all—I could just ignore him and the whole problem would go away.

If I just swam, jumped, and played in the waterfall area, would they even notice me?

I walked past them, my towel in my hand, the rock so hot under my feet that it burned.

Erik Krumel stared back at me in disbelief. He looked at me as though I had walked out of a dream. He could not believe his good fortune. The cigarette that dangled from his lips dropped. Team Krumel around him noticed he had stopped talking and turned to look at me as I passed.

"There he is," Erik hissed as I stepped past them, like they had been talking about me. By this time, I was both terrified and flattered. Krumel took an inventory of who was watching. He threw his glance around the park, searching for what I had already found out—there was no practicing authority figure on patrol.

The four, big guys with him watched me with shark-like eyes; there was prey in the area. The look in their faces held a level of disdain and disappointment.

"That little fucker?" one of them commented.

"Hey, Finucie, you are a hard guy to find," Krumel called out. I stopped, and turned toward him. I had to respond now.

"Nah, I'm everywhere."

I moved to go past but he moved out fast toward me. My hands came up to my shoulders and I opened my palms in a defensive gesture. I absorbed the first two punches he threw with my forearms. One snuck through and snapped against my lip, opening it up. I absorbed it as I landed a front kick to his stomach. He had not anticipated that.

His landed-punch had cost me dearly; blood was running over my chin.

"I always hated you," he bellowed with a high-pitched tone of a tell-tale, collapsed diaphragm. The kick had scored something anyway.

"Of course you would. I'm everything you wish you could be."

Blood flew off my lips with the last word. I threw a glance at the kids he was with. They were enjoying this. The older Krumel was only watching little brother handle this.

"Pete is not a big scrapper," I called. "There was no cause to beat him up. He didn't earn that from you. He's only half your size." I said the last part really loud to call attention to this fact right now.

"Everybody gets what they deserve, Finucan," he taunted and stepped closer.

I had to cut off the cavalry. An image flashed in my mind of being beaten by the crew and thrown in the murky water.

"How much do you weigh?" I asked him as he moved in.

Krumel was a wrestler and I knew he understood the importance of weight division and advantage.

"Don't worry, kid, we'll stay out of it," older Krumel said, then laughed. "Yeah, we got the family name to be concerned about."

"Oh, I won't need any help," Erik replied. He charged and threw several punches. I blocked the first two with my forearms, moved in and landed two of my own, then threw a kick to his leg.

I glanced down at the rocks. My buddies were swimming. John was talking to a cute redhead.

"What kind of guy needs help fighting someone half their body weight, unless they were really a pussy? I called out to Erik's older brother. Maybe it was better to involve him in it after all. I needed something crazy to happen.

Erik came with heavy hands of war that flew like flesh-colored, ball-peen hammers. He was no slouch. They were unfettered haymakers of gross motor skills that flew without any specific destination, and hit me randomly.

They landed on my forearms and glanced off the side of my head as I covered up and peered out between my hands, watching him advance. I knew I had to get inside to land any blows. I feigned moving backward, then half-stepped in toward him. I timed it between the rhythms of his swings; the sparring had taught me footwork.

When I got in, I landed three, up-close punches that sent him back on his heels. But he recovered and responded with a haymaker that made it around my guard and wrung me hard. The smell of burning metal filled my senses and a strong feeling of déjà vu overwhelmed me.

The world tilted to the right about forty degrees.

My guard dropped. With my guard down, the rest of the match is a blur. Today I wear a scar that looks like I had soft palate surgery. The red granite slapped my face. A kick blasted into my side and then my shoulder. I was moving, trying to protect my damaged head. My arms, at last, came up to guard my melon and a kick blasted into my forearms, slamming them against my head.

I tried to find my feet and pull my legs up underneath me, but more kicks pummeled my stomach, side, and back. His feet were bare. I blocked with my elbows—a karate trick. His little, pink toes didn't do the damage he was known for without the steel-toed boots.

Being kicked on the ground is an unforgettable feeling that changes you. But at last, even team Krumel had had enough.

"He's had enough, cowboy," someone finally said. Erik Krumel was pulled off me. I breathed in and felt pain in a lung. I remembered the punch to the throat Thompson had hit me with that crushed my voice box a few weeks ago.

Onlookers snickered. A tab on a beer can was popped and I heard a hissing of air come out of it.

The palms of my hands felt the smooth surface of the aged granite; I had a point of reference. My head was so heavy I could not lift it. I had to turn the rest of my body on my side, shifting the weight to my right. I felt my brain roll over in my skull, cloaked in pain.

I suppressed a groan. The fuckers would get nothing from me. Nothing. I pushed with my hands and felt my hips rise up, yet I could not lift my forehead off the ground. A family walked past me, pretending not to see me. This was "the way of the warrior" I learned that day.

I found my way to my feet and looked around for my towel. They were still holding Krumel back, like he wanted to tear into me yet.

"This ain't over, Finucan," he yelled.

"Anytime, fuckhead," I heard myself say; my voice sounded like Allan Hale, the Skipper, talking to Gilligan. "Okay, Little Buddy." But there was a sense of completion. I had faced him and he wasn't that bad. Getting my ass kicked was not as humiliating as taking shit from someone because you were scared to face them.

I got my feet going under me and treaded away on a cloud of pain. I walked the wrong direction for the first few steps. I saw the friends that I had ridden with and corrected my flight. Gravity pulled me heavily to one side or the other, and I extended my hands to my sides—like a tight rope walker.

I expected to hear laughter from behind me, but all I could hear was the pounding of the blood through my aching brain and the rush of the water of the Eau Claire Dells over the rocks.

I sat down next to John Purcell with a dazed smile. He hadn't seen the scuffle and it took a few minutes before he realized I was bleeding from the lip and head. I looked at the double images of the people sitting around and felt the sun on my wounded scalp.

I also felt a strong feeling of nausea sweep over me. I leaned over and purged the contents of my stomach (the McDonald's we stopped at on the way up) into a small, still pool of warm water, full of algae, about three-feet wide. The bile wretched up from within my core. When I was done, I wiped my mouth on my towel, blew my nose tenderly in it, and looked up. I saw the double images of my friends and smiled. My head felt better.

My friend's faces held expressions of horror, and they were all aimed at me. Words reached my ears—questions, what happened? What is wrong with you?" John looked back to survey the Krumel crowd.

"I thought you were right behind me. I missed it. What happened?" His head expanded and shrunk in my vision.

There was a sense of victory in my concussion. Though bitter-sweet, sweet no less.

"I have met the enemy, and he is me," I responded.

You didn't go to the Dells of the Eau Claire River and not go swimming, no matter what the occasion.

I found balance on the uneven, polished rock and stepped to the edge and jumped. I had forgotten about the rock ledge just below the shelf we were on. It extended out toward the water another two feet and I barely cleared it with my wounded head.

The turbulent, brown water seemed to cradle me when I trusted it and cascaded down into the depths. I drifted in the downward eddy. I relaxed to let the river have me. The current embraced me, spilling me over the second set of waterfalls in a heap. I was rolled by the light and soft, ancient water.

I kicked my feet and hit my knee on the top of a rock, but I caught the ledge that would let me out, and I clung to it like a zebra mussel. I raised myself out of the water. The world tilted again as I got out of the river and the stabbing pain in my lung seared a hot, branding-iron image in my mind.

During the ride home, I seemed to be watching myself from outside of the window, floating alongside the car. For a moment, I thought I was having an out-of-body experience, until I realized that I was looking at my reflection in the window.

But I belted out "He Ain't Heavy" with the Jacoby boys and kept in key. We had to stop one more time while I threw up. Then we stopped at Harry's Burgers on the way home. I had forgotten to bring money and my two, good friends covered my expenses.

I felt loved once again. Love tasted like head pain and an icy Coca-Cola from a Styrofoam cup with a straw in a paper wrapper.

There was a triumph somewhere in the afternoon, but I was too injured to find it this day.

That night I dreamt of running through a forest away from a wolf. It overtook me as I reached water. I held its snarling head away from my face as I plunged down into the icy, cold water. Somehow, I got away and climbed out onto a wilderness shoreline. I stood up to see Trish Lawton staring at me. She lifted her hand to show me a gift, but wouldn't open her hand to let me see it.

She stood there talking to me in a language I couldn't understand, with her hand glowing.

CHAPTER 22

Throwing down your sword is also an act of war. If you have attained mastery of swordlessness, you will never be without a sword. The opponent's sword is your sword. This is acting at the vanguard of the moment.

The Book of Five Rings, Miyamoto Musashi

Whenever you sit down to write, always approach it with the proper respect.

August Wilson

From the blue notebook:

Goss Joe showed Jenny Wilson the photographs of her husband making out with his secretary.

"That's him kissing her in Stange's Park, right by where I caught that fourteen-inch brook trout." Jenny looked at the photos and shrieked in grief.

"But he was rich and had an ivy league background. How could he cheat on me?" she sobbed so sweetly.

"Sorry, Mrs., uh, Johnson, was it? But clearly that's your husband Roger's hand on her booby, rolling the nipple in his fingers…"

""I can see damn well what it's doing, Joe!" She shrieked and threw herself at him. Joe caught her like the mainstay he was, like he could have been to Jenny if only she wasn't such a bitch.

* * *

The city pool was bathed in a single, lonely light, making it look like an abandoned fortress. The chlorinated water glistened behind the twelve-foot cyclone fence. The diving boards stood with no line at the ladder. They spoke like *The Giving Tree* to come play on them.

I flew on my bike down through the parking lot, rolling on the silent wheels through the sweet summer night, my dad close behind me. I leaned hard, cutting the angle up to the old cement bridge that led to Stange's Park. We were coming in the back way—better to leave our bikes here, on this side. They were not so visible from 3rd street where the cops patrolled.

After I dropped the bike on the mowed grass, I stepped over it and crouched low. I hit the fence with a little too much drama, showing off for the old man, and jammed my toes into the chain link. I scaled it fast and vaulted over the top. I climbed down a few more steps, then dropped on the inside of the fence. I was in.

Dad was impressed, but he took it easy. He was in good shape for a middle-aged guy, but there was no sense in getting hurt. He did good, making his way over it with a big smile on his face. He was robbing the institution of something. He was exacting some kind of rebellious revenge. We were breaking the law.

I dove off the high dive, soaring up into the dark sky, holding the swan. I hung there, before gravity claimed me, and drank the thrill of never knowing when to break out of the dive and spear my arms forward. I crashed through the dark, water-like glass breaking around me. I opened my eyes and saw nothing, but felt the familiar sting of the chlorine deep in the eye sockets. I fell deeper into the abyss until the inertia stopped and, for a moment, I was suspended in the night water, supported in a weightless womb.

Bliss overcame me and all the healing pain abated. Dad crashed down into the water somewhere near me. I surfaced and

I heard his whoop of exhilaration from the cold water in the hot night air.

Dad performed his flawless cannon ball that he had been perfecting since he was a kid—in the same swimming holes I did around Merrill. After the displaced water slapped down the pool side, he swam to the side with a grin as big as mine. At times like this, nothing separated us from being the best of friends. The boundary was still there—he was still in charge, and on big stuff, when he felt he needed to, he exerted his influence and demanded I follow rules that he valued. And I respected him for that.

"Check this out," I called and did my ole "one and a half," we called it—a flip forward from the high board that ended with a dive. I didn't spin hard enough and ended with the slap of my face on the dark water surface. Dad did his can opener, a difficult technique that when mastered, could throw water out with precision wherever you wanted it to go. A good can opener was a lifeguard soaker.

Dad bounced on the board once, then again, then sprang up and out in the night, while pointing the direction the dispersed wave would go. For a few seconds, he hung in mid-air, like an aerial Babe Ruth in a swimsuit. He seemed to defy the laws of gravity, posing with one hand pointed to the north. He seemed to allow gravity to take him down toward it, but just before he hit the water, he tucked his knee up tight to his chest and extended his other leg out, then leaned back hard. He broke the water's surface with grace that belied the sound that followed.

The wave thundered out of the pool and slapped the concrete deck like a humpback whale tail.

Dad and I were feeding on the energy and exhilaration from the stimulus of jumping from heights and plunging into cool water. Having so much fun I wondered if it was too much fun. I stopped on my way to the high dive and looked out into the park. The moonlit park was too quiet.

A shadowy figure of a man moved from one tree to the next, taking cover in the soft blue moonlight, moving toward us. Forty yards over, another figure moved to stalk behind another tree. Two men were approaching sneakily, and that was creepy. I was expecting cops with flashlights, squad cars and authority. I expected a barricade and bullhorn over the hood.

"All right, you kids, we know you're in the pool, so come out slow so we can see ya," the cop would say, calling out to us from behind flashing blue and red lights.

"Hey, someone's coming. We gotta go," I said in a harsh whisper as Dad surfaced from his cannon ball. We moved fast for the fence. It rattled when our hands and feet hit it.

My swimming trunks caught on the top of the fence and I ripped the crotch out of my shorts. We landed and jumped on our bikes as the two shadowy figures broke from their cover and ran silently toward us, like clown figures from *A Clockwork Orange*.

I envisioned zombie Indians running low at us with half-decayed faces and tomahawks in hand, covering the ground fast, because ghosts don't need to touch the ground when they run. I got the creeps and pedaled hard. But they were on foot and we had wheels beneath us, so we blew away the pursuers. We wound our way through the blocks of homes and quiet, dark city streets toward my house.

We laughed and relived the experience when we got to Judy and Bob's house. We pantomimed, talked about how it felt, and reveled in the excitement for a few minutes. But in the middle of it, Dad lit up a cigarette and looked distantly at the house I was going into.

There were lights on inside and a family milled about, moving past the windows. Dad's mood crashed like a DC-9 with an engine out.

"I sure screwed things up," he murmured. His tone came from the depths of a broken soul in despair. The smile slid from my face. The adventure lived out was now lost. My influence couldn't reach him there anymore.

"We sure ditched those guys back at the pool, didn't we?" I declared. "You have that can opener down right. Where did you learn that?"

But the darkness had descended. There was no grappling hook that could pull him back now.

"I'm going to find some place to sleep. Goodnight, Jamie." Dad pedaled quietly off on his bike down the driveway with a lit cigarette clenched in his teeth. He hunched over his handlebars, a broken man with the weight of a failed life draped about him. I wondered where he would sleep tonight. The homeless thing in the summer could be fun sometimes, until it was time to sleep. I went inside and crawled into my nice, warm, soft bed.

I slept until about three o'clock, then awoke, not knowing this pattern of interrupted sleep would haunt me throughout life. I took my blue notebook and Bic pen outside in the still summer moonlight and wrote about the dream I had just had.

I dreamed I needed to cross a river that was running swiftly. There was someone on the other side I needed to get to—the faceless figure waiting for me on the shoreline. I jumped off a tree limb and tried to swim across the current, but it kept pushing me downstream. I swam a crawl stroke hard, then look up to see the figure waving at me, getting smaller.

CHAPTER 23

Shawn was recovering from the boxing match and was healing from the concussion that kept him on his back in his room for several days. When he got up, he moved with a contemplated methodical style around the house and made yogurt and whole-grain bread.

He acted as the regulator when Tim and I fought and it got out of hand. He had pulled Tim off an assault and tossed him across the living room on more than one occasion. He went on to join the Marines and died in a tragic shooting accident at the age of 24, shortly after his four-year stint in the service.

The few memories of conversations I had with him I locked in a box in my mind and tried to preserve from the dust of time. But, today, I remember his gentle and kind qualities more than anything. His death further crippled my father and showed my mother to have an endless strength and optimism that is a mainstay for my own mentality today.

At the end of that summer, I remember him content and contemplative. Tim was also tranquil, humbled with his hand recovering from a limb-threatening injury. Deirdre was getting on track and changing her life around, and we were adjusting to the continuous turbulence of life. We were the functioning dysfunctional.

In that very summer, we were forming who we would become. In the upcoming years, my siblings left for college, or the service, and I was left behind with Dad in my hometown to make my own future.

But that summer was full of odd circumstances that fortified my identity and, in those moments, I chose who I was. I would be ashamed, or live with my legacy. I took on life and the people and things that stood before me, or I would break under them. I could wring fun and joy from this world and push down the specter of despair, or give in to the delicious self-serving of wallowing in sadness.

I was forging the metal that I would use in life. And I knew it.

The days were getting shorter and the sky more opaque. The long shadows reached from the trees in the yard and at the swimming holes, like fingers of Nosferatu toward us. Fall's stern kiss could be felt in the still, cool mornings. The dreaded daily countdown to the start of the school year was the unmentioned horror in all of our minds.

How to stop time during the summer? There was no solution.

I wanted a cherry, old-fashioned soda, so I walked across the street to the Dairy Queen. The sky was clear and the sun felt like the caress of God. Jenny Wilson was working, but I went to the other window. Jenny glanced at me as she dipped a cone of the soft-serve in a cherry covering.

She looked again and smiled. She had heard about the fight with Krumel. She was one of the ladies who liked to see the blood. They gathered in the hallways and watched in a hungry trance when you were in a fistfight for your life. It turned them on or something.

I tried to smile, but the stitches on my lip hurt when I did. I gave up.

I looked away and accepted my soda. The thrill was gone. She was too rich for my blood. She was too hoity-toity for a Finucan to have. She was out of my league. And I was okay with that. There was power in acceptance. There was comfort in not trying to be something I wasn't.

I had learned that the girls on "my side of the tracks" were a lot of fun.

*   *   *

I jumped the stairs up to the porch of Trish Lawton's house and smelled shrimp cooking inside. The Border Collie welcomed me, extracting a pat on the head as a toll to get by. I knocked on the screen door; it banged against the frame with each knock. Through the screen I could see her dad sleeping on the couch.

An impulse made me want to knock again, hard enough to wake up that piece of shit, but Trish came to the door in a red-and-yellow, spotted sundress with a sash that tied at her waist. She had this plastic thing in her hair that matched her dress, and her dark eyes smiled. I forgot to breathe for just a second.

I remembered the broken-egg-yolk, orange-marmalade-splashed sunset I had seen spreading out behind us on the lake when John Purcell and I were fishing on the Wisconsin River a few days before.

Her smile was genuine; she didn't know how to pretend. In my unspoken need, I drank that in. We stood there smiling at each other without saying anything for a long moment. Her dad snored in the background. Neither of us wanted to shatter this welcome with words. I barely found my breath as we stared at each other. She was doing the same; I could feel it. That knowledge ignited something in me—something primal. Something I had yet to understand.

Rather than invite me in, she stepped out onto the crooked porch and silently closed the door behind her. She smoothed her hands over her dress and sat down on the swing that hung from rusty chains.

"You look nice," I commented.

"Thanks. It's a travel day for me. I am taking a bus to New Orleans to live with my mom. What happened to your face?"

She reached out and touched the bruise on my face, above the split lip that Krumel had scored in the fight. I sat down next to her, hiding the trauma I felt from the news. Somehow I had gotten skilled at that.

The swing moved beneath us. I was glad she didn't want to talk about the library argument that involved my notebook.

"I fell down, kind of. Do you have to leave?"

She hesitated before speaking, then wiped a tear from her face with three fingertips together. She was too good at that.

"Yes, it's better for me down there. Dad's getting worse." Another tear rolled down her nose and she caught it with her fingers again. "But my bus will pick me up at the gas station downtown. You could walk me there if you will help me with my bag. Then I don't have to wake up my dad," she offered with a smile that broke my heart for the first time in my life, but not the last.

"I would like that," I replied.

"It's a big bag to carry. Are you sure?"

"Yeah. I'm very strong."

I put my arm around her. She melted against me, and as we walked together, I did feel strong.

* * *

In my blue notebook I wrote:

"I wanted to meet you here at Zettler's bakery because this is where my husband proposed marriage to me, Mr. McFlynn. We sat here at this table. He sat where you are sitting now," Jenny Wilson said. "I am hopeful that you have some information on the assassination of my ex-husband."

"As a matter of fact, I do have some progress to report. It was an inside job." The plate of eggs with pork sausage patties and wheat toast was set in front of Joe and he let it distract him. "Can I get some Tabasco sauce?" Joe asked the waitress.

"You sure can, Joe," she said and winked at him. He was peppering his eggs, then glanced up to see Jenny staring at him with an expectant expression.

"Well, whoever shot him through the glass knew he was going to be there. The prints in the dirt walk right to the window. The killer was short, from the gait of the stride, perhaps five-foot-five."

"I don't think we have anyone in our employ of that size, Joe," she said and smiled gently.

"Oh, if you are referring to the groundskeeper that you are having relations with, no, he is much taller," Joe responded and stuffed a mouthful of eggs into his face, then picked up the toast and smeared orange marmalade jelly on it. The waitress set down the hot sauce. Joe spun the cap off and splashed it on everything on his plate.

"I beg your pardon," Jenny said, but with no surprise in her voice.

"The two goons you sent to my apartment last night…I kicked the crap out of both of them. I felt bad afterwards and bought them a pizza. We had a few beers and laughed our asses off."

The plate of food began disappearing like smoke in a car with a cracked open window as Joe wolfed it down.

"They told me you sent them. You were pissed because you think I told Ronnie Tompkins that you and I were making out in the stadium. You are mad that I told those guys that you pulled away from me when I tried to touch your booby. You were mad that I shared that, so you sent them to kick my ass. Teach me a lesson."

Joe looked at her face when he spoke but told himself to not be a putz.

"They get these eggs delivered from the Smith Farm—no kidding. It's why this place does good business," Joe said around a mouthful of food. "I mean, did you ever see yellows like this?"

Joe mopped up the yellow eggs with the last bite of wheat toast.

"So you figured it out. So what. Do you think you will live long enough to tell someone?" She produced a small automatic pistol from her purse and aimed it at Joe. Jenny sat there with her hand extended and a napkin over it. "We are going to walk out of here, nice and slow."

Under the table, Joe slipped off his shoes and wiggled his toes in his yellow, crusted socks.

"At least now, you're doing your own dirty work," Joe said. "Or isn't that what you did with Brenda Thompson, too? She beat you out of the cheerleading squad, then turns up dead at Blue Boats from a bench in the water?"

Jenny began to cough now. The stench from Joe's feet reached her, wafting up from under the table like poison mustard gas, making her instantly nauseous.

"What on earth is that awful smell?" she choked out, but the last part of the sentence pinched off in a saliva shift somewhere in her throat.

"The human body can't actually produce such an odor," she gasped. The gun in her hand wavered. The napkin fell off.

"It's people's behavior that stinks. And your actions smell like a gut pile in the summer sun," Joe said wiggling his toes.

Joe could feel a pleasing hot steam of perspiration come off his feet, flooding him in a sensation of relief.

"These dogs are steaming," he said.

"Shut up, you wicked brute, and put your damn shoes on now, or I shall be forced to shoot us both out of any decency I have left for human kind."

She bull-frogged up the muffin she had for breakfast. Her cheeks filled then collapsed as she re-swallowed it.

"Any shred of decency left you long ago," Joe countered. A lady at the next table, eating a chocolate-covered donut with yellow custard oozing from an open bite, began to gag and choke. Her male friend got up from the table and wretched a dry heave before running to the bathroom, lifting his shirt to cover his mouth as he ran. He vomited into his shirt and wings of puke shot out behind his head, like the FTD floral man. The dining room instantly filled with the sharp, yucky stench of almost-digested food.

Jenny Wilson looked away from Joe, searching for the ladies' bathroom and measuring her distance from it. Joe reached out and snatched the pistol out of her hand. With her gloved hand over her mouth, she tried to slide out of the booth.

Joe reached over, caught her wrist in his grip, and held her in the booth. She struggled for a few seconds, then passed out from the overwhelming toxic odor. She collapsed on the vinyl seat cover. The classy nature she had displayed was gone.

Joe slid out of the booth, moved his shoes out from under the table, and slid them on. Then he reached into his wallet, pulled out a five-dollar bill and tossed it onto the table.

"Remember, they don't call me Gross Joe for nothing," he said and walked out of the diner.

"Thanks, Joe. See you soon, hon," the cute waitress called around chewing her gum and gave him a wink over her shoulder. Joe had decided that she was quite adorable.

* * *

Dad and I sat on the memorial to the unborn at the cemetery. I had crafted two peanut-butter-and-jelly sandwiches (heavy on the peanut butter) and carved off two big hunks of sharp cheddar cheese. The knife moved through the master chunk like in a commercial. I wrapped them in plastic film and hauled them in a paper sack on my bike. After eating them, we washed them down with warm cans of Coke.

By late August, the air had a chill of the ending of summer, like a mother calling to a child to come away from the swing set. Summer had to go. The days were not so bright and the blue sky had just a touch of opaque light.

The blue from the sky seemed to melt into the water. On the lake, whitecaps sparked in the sun and I watched them roll under my friend's dock, like an endless conveyor belt of fascination. The season of magic was passing.

I smelled crisp maple-tree bark in the breeze, and in the smell of fresh-cut grass I could detect the tarry smell of walnut juice dripping from the trees.

"I have to go," Dad said. "I can't stay here in the winter. I will freeze my ass."

He bit into the bread. I didn't say anything. I imagined what it would feel like to have to leave my home town and find someplace to live by myself with no friends.

"Where will you go?"

"I am going to get some money from some people who want me to create a tax shelter for them. I will do that and get a few thousand dollars. With that, I can live within means out on the beach in San Onofre Park in San Clemente, California. It's warm there and I can live out of a tent."

"What do you do all day there?"

"Hang out, read, and watch people. There are a lot of pretty women out there in California—some outstanding ladies that make your head spin around. The women out there keep in shape. Out there, the gals don't leave a guy after they marry him."

"When will you be back?"

"I'll come back in the spring, as soon as it starts getting warm. I'll be thinking about you kids all the time when I'm out there. You have to know that."

I was losing my best buddy, and my help.

"I will miss you," I admitted and finished off the sandwich. Sometimes heartbreak went with a meal.

"I'll be back. You won't be able to reach me, so stay out of trouble. I'll call from time to time."

A blue jay landed in a cherry tree and beeped at us.

"I had a good summer hanging with my little buddy," Dad added.

"I had a great summer, too," I replied, looking at my best friend—my dad.

* * *

The summer ended as quickly as a waterslide. The nights cooled off deliciously and brought slumber to the evenings, and the mornings held the threat of autumn until the sun warmed the mid-day. Then, like a surprise ending in a symphony, it was over.

That summer I learned there is a reckoning. I am not the same person leaving the summer as I was going into it. I could touch a loss of naivety someplace inside. I had aged, and felt it for the first time. I played out the remaining days of that summer knowing I was leaving the boy behind.

And when I sat down to write on the picnic table in the early morning moonlight, I found that I didn't write. I sat there thinking about Trish Lawton. I wondered what she was doing right then, and if she could see the moon.

And then school began.

I was attending the Merrill Junior High, a bigger school than I had ever been in, with kids being bussed in from all over the county. I had no friends, all having been left back at the Catholic school. Strangers surrounded me as I wandered the halls, not knowing where to go or where I was supposed to be, and I had a sneaking suspicion that I might have a learning deficiency when it came to math.

But there were girls here at this school. More than I had seen at one time—all different shapes, sizes and personalities. Some of them were incredible, and just when you sat next to the most beautiful one, you later shared a science lab table with another that spoke German and wore a cheerleader outfit.

I asked them questions to hear their voices. When a girl walked by, if I stayed still, I could smell her perfume. Some of them smelled like sunshine, others like rain. There was a sweet breeze from a redhead that almost resembled lilac, but not quite.

But wherever there is beauty, there is danger.

Benson found me in the lunch room. I had a tray with a plastic plate of lasagna that actually looked good, some yellow garlic bread, a small leafy salad, a bowl with a few canned peach slices, and a little carton of chocolate milk. I had forgotten to eat for a day and was famished. I sat at an empty table. Benson sat down across from me with two of his friends.

A hush of expectation settled over the crowd in the lunch room. Benson looked at me across the table with his head cocked to the side, like the dog looking at an old phonograph. His head was big and blockish, almost seeming to have square corners. His eyes were fierce green and they locked on mine, looking for fear.

"Hey, Finucie, I've been looking for you. All I had to do was wait till school started." He tipped his palms up and looked around. "Now that you are here, I like school a lot more. You know why that is?"

"Because you could learn to spell your own name," I replied. No one laughed. "I'd ask you if it's Benson, or Bensen with an "e", but I don't think you know." Benson's hand shot out toward me, knocking my lasagna against my chest. As it slid down, I caught it and flipped the wad of pasta toward him. It spattered on his Kiss shirt.

Benson was reaching across the table for me when I stood up with the closed milk carton and whipped it into his face. I threw it like the Brewers pitcher, Jerry Augustine, burning one into the glove of Larry Haney. At the time I let the carton go, Benson's face looked like a catcher's glove, and I felt the rage quenched in that moment.

The milk carton hit Benson in the mouth and exploded on impact. I was getting to my feet when the kid on my left punched the side of my head. The other kid swung at me, but missed when I moved. I tried to get up, but fell down. They both got up and starting kicking me with fast, hard soccer kicks. The crowd jeered and someone laughed. A pretty girl came into focus, watching me getting my ass kicked—liking it. It was Jenny Wilson.

An hour later I was in the vice principal's office, waiting to be invited to tell my side of the story.

I was the new kid in the public school. I had been here all of three hours, I was involved in an altercation, and I was being marked as a problem. I remember feeling hungry as I had to wait; I didn't get to eat my damn lunch. It was going to be a long year.

* * *

I finished flipping through the 38-year-old blue notebook and let the cover fall closed. The paper landed softly; the time capsule shut, the portal sealed.

I smiled at my mother and thanked her for giving it to me. The echoes of Dad's laughter faded and the summer of innocence called out to be remembered—in case I had forgotten who I was.

ACKNOWLEDGEMENTS

I thank my mother, Judy Weaver, for believing in this project.

I especially thank my wife, the only soft edge in my life.

Thanks to Bob Weaver for all his patience and kindness through the years.

Special thanks to Tim and Deirdre for laughter, understanding and tribal support.

This book would not be possible if not for the tireless, endless hours of focus and commitment of my editor, Ralph Yearick. He poured over the manuscript with his gentle, correcting touch, making the work clear and concise without changing my writing voice. He took the time not just to correct the errors but to educate me and help me become a better writer. Ralph handled this project with the mastery of a literary black belt and the delicacy of a word surgeon. There is no finer editor with a keener eye for detail on the planet today. Thanks, Ralph.

About the Author

Jim Finucan is the author of three published books including *Interview Strategy: The Next Move is Yours*; *The Spear* (fiction); and *Past Due!: A Debt Collecting Manual for Business Professionals.*

Wild Counselor is a gripping, honest memoir in which Finucan recounts the childhood summer that defined him as he watched his father fall from status of prominent attorney to homeless man sleeping in the parks and struggling with a mental breakdown. A small business owner, he still lives in Merrill, where he and his wife have raised four children.

Jim hopes this work will aid in allowing people to see the homeless and broken as someone's dad, brother, son, daughter or friend. A portion of the royalties of this project will go toward supporting a homeless shelter being built in Merrill. The author is grateful for reader support.

47108817R00175

Made in the USA
Middletown, DE
07 June 2019